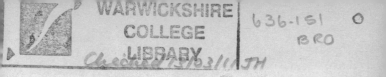

CROSSING
THE LINE

WITHDRAWN

CROSSING THE LINE

The World of Racing Revealed

CHARLIE BROOKS

HEADLINE

Copyright © 1999 Charlie Brooks

The right of Charlie Brooks to be identified as the Author
of the Work has been asserted by him in accordance with the
Copyright, Designs and Patents Act 1988.

First published in 1999
by HEADLINE BOOK PUBLISHING

First published in paperback in 2000
by HEADLINE BOOK PUBLISHING

10 9 8 7 6 5 4 3 2 1

ISBN 0 7472 6092 3

Typeset by Palimpsest Book Production Limited,
Polmont, Stirlingshire
Printed and bound in Great Britain by
Mackays of Chatham plc, Chatham, Kent

HEADLINE BOOK PUBLISHING
A division of the Hodder Headline Group
338 Euston Road
London NW1 3BH

www.headline.co.uk
www.hodderheadline.com

CONTENTS

ACKNOWLEDGEMENTS

This book could not have been written without the assistance of many people.

It all started at Charlie and Tita Carter's South American party. Dressed as an urchin, I couldn't help but notice a nubile, semi-naked Tequila girl across the room. That was how I was lucky enough to meet Sarah Wooldridge of IMG. She was standing next to her. Whether she thinks she was lucky is unlikely, but she agreed to act as my agent. *Crossing the Line* isn't what we'd originally planned it would be, but whatever is? Without Sarah it wouldn't have been anything at all, and I'm grateful to her for sticking with it.

This project would have been a non-starter without the guidance and help of Sean Magee: I can't thank him enough for his unflappable encouragement.

Thanks also to Mark Bradstock, Charlie Nelson, Brian Delaney and Graham Bradley for jogging my memory; to Barry Allen and Celia Marr for veterinary advice; to

Tom Jones and Tony Gilmore for permission to reproduce their poems; to Ian Marshall and Lorraine Jerram at Headline; to DCI Hamilton and the Serious Crime Squad for providing material for a first chapter just at thetime when I didn't know how the book should begin; to the landlords of the Tite Inn in Chadlington and the Chequers in Chipping Norton for providing fuel for the research; and to my mother, brother and sister for support throughout.

Most of all, thanks to Miriam for putting up with the whole process.

1
BAD FRIDAY

U NTIL I TURNED UP at my sister's house in London, Friday 8 January 1999 had been a pretty civilised day. The previous evening had been spent with an old school friend in the Cavalry and Guards Club, followed by a few drinks into the early hours at Tramp night-club, and then a good breakfast at Claridge's. I was off the mark for an enjoyable day, and strongly of the opinion that there were some advantages in not being tied to the relentless routine of a racing yard – a way of life I had given up nine months earlier.

After an excellent breakfast I set off in very good humour for Annabel's house – where the smile was wiped off my face by the look on hers as I walked through the door. It had very bad news written all over it. My initial reaction was: 'Who's died?' It was that sort of expression.

'Miriam's on the phone – you'd better speak to her.'

I went to the phone. Quite calmly – considering she had been awakened at six in the morning by the dogs barking and men beating on the cottage door – my girlfriend said: 'The police have been here.'

At first I couldn't take this seriously. 'Who did they want?' I asked. 'You or me?'

'You.'

Six hours later I found myself in a cold, damp cell at Charing Cross police station, trying to come to terms with the events and implications of the last few hours. I lay looking at the ceiling and thought to myself: 'What the fuck am I doing in here?'

It was pitch dark when the frantic barking of the dogs had woken Miriam up. At first she assumed that a fox was outside looking for breakfast – he usually got lucky when I was left in charge of shutting the chickens up at night – but then she heard banging on the door. From the window she could see torches flashing everywhere, and she thought that thieves were trying to nick her car. Annoyed and alarmed, she shouted out of the window: 'What the hell do you think you're doing?!'

'Police officers!' was the reply.

She told them to put their ID through the door (though not their hands as the dogs were getting very agitated). But the ID did not impress her sufficiently, so she told them they weren't coming in. Eventually Newbury police station confirmed that they were police with a genuine search warrant, so she let the three of them in and made them a cup of coffee.

'You seem very relaxed, madam,' the big one said.

'Of course I am,' replied Miriam. 'The sum total of Charlie's criminal activity to date is under-age drinking.

Thank God he's not here. He's a nervous lad. You'd have frightened him to death.'

Having drunk their coffee, the police proceeded to trawl through the cottage, collecting diaries, bank accounts and five fertiliser sacks full of paperwork accumulated over seven years at Uplands that the rats had been checking in the garage, all of which they took away with them. They didn't look in the gun cupboard. It is the only secure 'safe' in the cottage and probably the place where I'd have salted away my ill-gotten gains – had there been any.

Miriam sneaked into the yard to try and ring me – unsuccessfully, as at that moment I was sauntering around London looking forward to lunch with the Bow Lane Partnership, some friends I used to train for, to talk about buying them a new horse. But she kept trying, and now she had reached me at last.

My initial reaction was that it was very funny and quite exciting – part of the rich tapestry of life, and all that. But then she told me that jockeys Graham Bradley and Ray Cochrane had been arrested, and a host of very different thoughts started crashing around my mind.

Being pursued by police was simply something that happened to other people, not to me. A feeling of real anger started to take over as I reflected on the consequences. Whatever the eventual outcome, to be drawn into this sort of thing was going to leave a slur on my character. You didn't need to be Einstein to work out that this was all to do with the investigation into race-fixing and doping which by this stage had been going on for a year. Even if I was exonerated very soon, henceforth – in some people's minds, at least

– I would be known as the trainer who was arrested in the race-fixing investigation, rather than the trainer who had sent out two Hennessy winners and a horse that had not only been second in two Grand Nationals but had caught the hearts and imaginations of thousands of people. I would be Charlie Brooks who 'must have done something'; no smoke without fire, you know. It wasn't going to matter what happened from now on. I was going to have this round my neck for the rest of my life. On the immediate job front huge damage was going to be done, and in the long term it could wreck the chance of my ever being able to make a positive contribution to running racing, a role I would love to have played: having worked in racing for seventeen years, I felt there might have been something I could have contributed.

But worrying about the rest of my life could wait. Much more pressing was the practical consideration of what I was to do there and then.

My first impulse was simply to go off to Charing Cross police station (where the investigation was based) and see what it was all about.

Annabel was more pragmatic. If I was going to the police, she said, it was essential that I go with a lawyer.

Knowing which was the right lawyer was a problem. (As Peter Walwyn, the patriarch of Lambourn trainers, always points out in his inimitable way, you don't go to a heart surgeon if you have piles.) In the end we opted for our family solicitors in Lincoln's Inn Fields as a safe pair of hands. I went round to their offices and made an appointment to go to Charing Cross later in the day.

At three o'clock in the afternoon my solicitor and I duly presented ourselves at the police station, announced ourselves at the reception desk and were asked to wait. This struck me as being somewhat incongruous: a few hours before the police had been tracking me down by torchlight before dawn, and now I was being asked to sit patiently while they got round to arresting me!

After about ten minutes we were shown into the main body of the police station, where as soon as the door was shut behind us the ritual of the formalities began: 'Charles Brooks, I am arresting you on suspicion of . . .' – I was too bewildered to remember all the words – '. . . You are not required to say anything, but anything you do say may be taken down and . . .' Then the verbiage gave way to what felt like an endless session of filling in forms declaring all manner of things – mostly that I understood that I had been arrested. That much I did understand; but I certainly could not fathom why.

Ray Cochrane and Graham Bradley were waiting to be interviewed. I knew they were going to be there but they didn't know I was.

Brad laughed – as only Brad could – as I walked in: 'Hello, Charles, I didn't expect to meet you here.'

A blackboard read 'Cochrane Cell 1', then 'Bradley Cell 2' – then there was a blank. Obviously I was headed for Cell 3.

'See you've been drawn low, Ray,' I said – then was told not to talk to him.

Before my interview started I had discussed with my lawyer what the police were likely to want to talk about. I got that completely wrong. It seemed to me that they had come to the conclusion that I was a central figure in the whole race-fixing investigation, as four out of five of the jockeys who had been arrested had ridden for me –

including Ray Cochrane, who had once ridden a winner for me, though I had very few runners on the Flat. But the police informed my lawyer that they only wanted to talk to me about one race, at Warwick over two years earlier, in which I had run a horse called Man Mood.

As soon as I heard the name I groaned. Not that horse again!

The Oliver Cromwell Chase at Warwick on 5 November 1996 had just two runners. Man Mood started 7–4 on favourite to beat 5–4 chance Drumstick, and was leading until his jockey Graham Bradley pulled him up before the twelfth fence, with about a mile still to run, leaving Drumstick to go on and win. There had been, it was said, a disproportionate amount of money bet on the outsider of the pair.

Man Mood's defeat had seemed perfectly explicable to me – he was a horse whose career had been blighted by recurrent respiratory problems and I could not fancy him at all for the Warwick race – but to some bookmakers the result smelled, and now the two detectives grilling me in that interview room wanted to know all about it.

What were my instructions to Brad before the race?

Was I happy with the way the horse had been ridden?

Had I had a bet in the race – on my horse or on the other one?

Had I cooperated with the subsequent Jockey Club investigation into the race (which had found nothing amiss)?

I engaged in a lengthy discussion about Man Mood and his problems, and then the detectives came to the point.

They had been told that Graham Bradley and I, along with unnamed others, had colluded to fix the race.

That's simply not true, I insisted, but the police wanted to know more. In particular, they were keen to investigate closely my attitude to the Jockey Club investigation. I pointed out that I had talked at great length to the Jockey Club and had shown them the veterinary evidence of Man Mood's condition. Man Mood had run badly early in 1996, and we'd sent him to the veterinary experts at Bristol University for a detailed examination. There he had been put on the equine treadmill and his respiratory system closely monitored, but nothing conclusive had come to light. First time out that season, ten days before the Warwick race, he had run at Worcester, where he'd drifted in the market from 6–1 out to a starting price of 14–1 before running abominably, beaten about thirty lengths.

The Jockey Club interviewed my staff who had worked with the horse, and all confirmed the same picture: he gurgled badly at home and hated having his tongue tied down, though he had shown improved form when running with a tongue-strap after the Warwick race. The reason we had not run him at Warwick with his tongue tied down was that at the time a tongue-strap always made the horse very tense. And so on and so on and so on.

The bottom line was that Man Mood hardly had the right to be odds-on favourite for the Warwick race. He'd run like a drain at Worcester and was suffering from familiar problems – and in any case Drumstick had enough decent form to be favourite himself. Though a bit of an old shit of a horse, Drumstick was at least a consistent old shit.

So why run Man Mood at all? It looked like a bad race, and we thought that maybe he'd relax in a small field and be spared the old breathing problem.

All this – and much more – I told the police, and after about three-quarters of an hour of questioning the interview came to an end.

But the ordeal was far from over. I had to stay on at the police station in case they wanted to ask me any more questions; this meant emptying my pockets so they could lock me in a cell. As I was filling in yet more forms Brad was sitting behind me.

'You won't find much cash on him,' I heard him joke before his solicitor told him not to talk to me. (Like the Royal Family, I have a reputation for travelling without cash, especially in the pub on the way back from racing.)

Damp, cold and smelly, the walls decorated with graffiti, a single window too high to offer any reasonable view of the outside world: the cell was as miserable a place as I'd ever been in. As I lay there, baffled, humiliated and furious, the anger surged up inside me. What the hell was I doing there, and who was behind it?

Some things started to fall into place – like a curious incident a couple of days earlier. Miriam had gone out during the morning, and phoned me from the village to report that she had just been stopped by two men in a car who had asked her if she knew where Pounds Farm was: they were looking for Charlie Brooks. Having helped them out, she promptly called to warn me that two unfamiliar individuals were on their way up to see me. They never arrived, but Miriam's description of one of them matched a policeman I had just seen upstairs in the police station . . .

I could dream up all sorts of coincidences, ponder all sorts of outcomes, but I could not get over this basic fact – that I was stuck in a revolting cell in a police station in the middle of London.

In due course they let me go, at which point I suddenly remembered that my mother was returning that day from a trip to Egypt and going straight from the airport to a party. I had to get hold of her before she heard the news on the radio or saw the evening paper. Eventually I tracked her down.

'Had a nice time? . . . Good . . . Yes, everything's fine here. Oh, one slight problem. Nothing to worry about really, but you should know that I was arrested today.'

She took this in her stride. She's used to her children springing surprises.

When I left the police station it was pissing down with rain, and I was soaking wet when I shoved myself on to the Tube.

I'd had no change to buy the *Evening Standard*, and had to crane my neck to read it over a young woman's shoulder.

Nothing on the back page. Phew.

Then she turned to the front page. Shit! – a photograph. I'm not sure whether it was the headline or the sight of my double chin which gave me the greater fright.

The woman heard my exclamation of horror, looked at me, looked back at the picture in the paper, and looked at me again.

Then she moved down the carriage.

2

CUSTARD AND COMPETITION

H ORSE RACING MIGHT NOT have been in my blood, but the sporting instinct certainly was.

My great-grandfather Marshall Brooks was an exceptionally gifted athlete. He was a rugby international, playing for England against Scotland in 1874, but specialised in the long jump and high jump. He was the first man ever to clear 6 feet in the latter event, and at the Oxford versus Cambridge athletics match at Crystal Palace in 1876 cleared 6 feet $2\frac{1}{2}$ inches, a world record. Never mind the Western Roll or the Fosbury Flop – Marshall Brooks had a more straightforward approach to the high jump, as an eye-witness of his record-breaking jump confirmed: 'He took a shortish run, straight, and rose almost upright over the bar, with his legs tucked underneath his body, both legs going over at the same time.'

A generation after Marshall Brooks, another of my sporting ancestors made his mark when my mother's father George Todd won the Indian Open golf tournament.

My grandfather ran (and my grandmother's family owned) the Bolsover Colliery in Derbyshire, and when after the Second World War the new Labour government nationalised the coal mines he moved south and bought a farm in Oxfordshire near Chipping Norton – which is where I was born on 3 March 1963, youngest of three children after my brother Christopher, now an artist, and my sister Annabel, an actress.

My earliest years were spent on the farm – then run by my father Robert Brooks – and as a small boy I loved nothing better than stacking hay bales, working the grain dryer with my father or riding on the combine harvester with our farmhand Herman Seidel. When my grandfather bought the farm Herman was already working there: he had been a prisoner of war – at nights he was locked up above the Shire horses – and after the war was over he did not want to go back to Germany. He married a local girl and settled down in the area, and as we went round the fields on the combine he would regale me with his memories: how as a young man he had been to Hitler's rallies to discover what Nazism was all about; how he had been shot in the stomach when fighting on the Russian front and had been on the last hospital train out – with his stomach wrapped in a hosepipe as the Germans had run out of medical supplies – before the army was overrun; how he had been returned to the front and been captured by the Americans.

Anxious to keep in touch with his homeland despite

not wanting to return there, Herman bought a huge radio with a gigantic aerial so that he could listen to broadcasts from Radio Germany – which worked fine until one evening the aerial was struck by lightning and Herman was blown out of bed.

One of Herman's stories had a poignant racing association – and an eerie connection with my own racing life. One summer evening in August 1962 the trainer Charlie Pratt was in a light plane returning to Lambourn from Redcar with a couple of his owners after their horse Songedor had won the valuable William Hill Gold Cup. The plane got into trouble over Oxfordshire and came down very near our farm, killing all the occupants. The first person on the scene was Herman Seidel, and he would later tell me how he saw, hanging there in the burnt out wreckage, the gold cup itself. By an extraordinary coincidence, Charlie Pratt was then the owner of Uplands, the Lambourn training yard that was to loom so large in my own life . . .

Horses, naturally enough, played an important role on the farm, and one of Herman's primary duties was to work the carthorses, notably a fine Shire named Prince. One day Herman had Prince harnessed to a grass cutter when the horse bolted, charging off into the nearest wood with Herman helplessly struggling to bring him back under control. The horse ran between two trees, writing off the machine and dislodging the hapless Herman – with the result that carthorses were dispensed with, and my grandfather bought a tractor. Even so, horses remained a vital part of farm life. Both my parents were keen members of the local hunt, the Heythrop, and were keen to encourage in me a love of riding.

I can't pretend that the level of encouragement was met with an equal level of enthusiasm. The simple fact was that from the moment I was first placed on a pony at the age of nought I hated riding, and I'd do anything I could to get out of it. One day I disgraced myself by riding my pony Dunlin full pelt into the yard and into his box, rather than winding him down after belting round the farm. As Dunlin stood in his barn heaving and sweating his pilot received a good old dressing-down from our groom Janet: 'Do that tomorrow and you'll never ride again!' Great, I thought – but I couldn't get out of it that easily, and eventually was subjected to the even greater pain of the Pony Club, my first taste of institutionalised horsiness. This meant bossy horsy women shouting at me all day – 'Come along, Charles! Heels down! Toes up!' I loathed it. One year I managed to tip my saddle off the wall into the muck clamp as we were loading up for Pony Club camp, and my father had to follow us to the camp later, once the location of the saddle had been extracted from me.

My dislike of horses when young boiled down to the fact that I was scared of them, and scared that they might run off with me. I was very weak, and was always being carted, which anyone who has ever ridden will know is one of the most frightening experiences going. I was also, as a small child, very reclusive and avoided the company of other children as much as possible – especially if they wanted to stage an impromptu pony race – but at the age of six it was time for some serious schooling, and I was enrolled at Kitebrook, near Chipping Norton.

I was not, to begin with, a very willing pupil, and on my first morning there did my level best to nip my education in the bud. As I was being taken into the school I managed to get my legs jammed against the door frame, and I clung to it like a limpet. The headmistress and my elder brother Christopher – already a veteran of four years at the school – pulled from one side as my mother pushed from the other, but I would not give in without a struggle, and with tears pouring down my face I screamed hysterically as the two sides dug in for a long fight. But there were three of them and only one of me, and eventually I had to bow to the inevitable and be dragged through the door.

Before long I was extremely glad that I had not had my way on that first morning, as the gender ratio was fifteen girls to every boy – sixty of them to just four of us – and innumerable sessions of 'you can look at mine if I can look at yours' proved highly educational.

The downside of Kitebrook was custard. My aversion to custard was deeply ingrained, and since it was an immovable and non-negotiable item of the lunch menu, the only solution was to spoon it into the pockets of my shorts when no one was watching. Inevitably I was caught doing this, and hauled off to the staff room to be disciplined. 'Charles, you're a very naughty boy' – and in a moment a large puddle had formed around my feet as tears poured down my fat little cheeks.

It was about this time that I was introduced to horse racing, through my grandmother. She was quite a punter, and on Grand National day 1969 took me to the betting shop at Moreton-in-Marsh, where between us we backed most of the runners before going back to her house at Stretton-on-the-Fosse to watch the race on television. I was hooked on the National from that day on, and determined that one day I would ride in it.

At the age of eight I left Kitebrook and went to board at Cothill, a prep school near Abingdon. My brother was already at the school, but there was little comfort in his presence: he forbade me to call him by his name Christopher, insisting that I address him as Brooks Major. Initially I was a weekly boarder, coming out on Saturdays for a precious few hours back on the farm, but I was so homesick that I could rarely get through the week without breaking down into a blubbing wreck by Thursday evening. (This habit of collapsing in tears stayed with me well into my late teens when I was at Eton – though by then they were tears of frustration and fury: returning to school after time at home was removing my freedom, just like being sent back to prison.)

In due course, though I constantly yearned to be at home working on the farm with my father, I bowed to the inevitable restrictions of boarding at Cothill and started to enjoy myself there. There were limits, however, and among the letters home which my mother has preserved from those days is this early expression of the Brooks stubborn streak, concerning a fellow pupil whom I shall call Barry Hodges:

Dear Mummy and Daddy

I hope you are well. I am. I was captain of the Under-11's and we won 6–0. We are in the middle of a film called *The Knights of the Round Table*. Arthur Pendragon has just married his wife. I got your letter just now and the last thing I want to happen is that Barry Hodges comes out with me. I forbid he does. I am on dead bad terms with him. Don't forget Daddy has got to pull the wild oats out of the Burford Road field. Please tell the builders that Man Utd will be OK. We beat Ajax 1–0 and lost away to Wolves 2–1. Peugeot's mother [Peugeot was a boy in my dorm] is pregnant. Hope the cattle food lasts out. I'm glad Daddy's tennis is going well. I'm sure Mummy's is too. Once again please change the arrangements. The last thing I wanted to do was to have anything to do with Barry Hodges. Someone else will take him out.

Lots of love
Charles

PS Of course I won't go out with Barry Hodges on the 25th and my radishes are doing well.

(This letter had another postscript. Over twenty years later I was sitting on a panel at a charity racing evening at Chipping Norton Theatre, and the same letter was read out as an example of my supposed independence of spirit. In the bar afterwards a complete stranger came up to me and said: 'You were right about that Barry Hodges: he's a complete tosser.' This man had been at college with him, and poor Barry had not made himself any more popular in the intervening years!)

Although I was a reclusive child I loved going to play with my mother's godson Francis Kirkpatrick: we nicknamed him 'Fritz' after a German in a war magazine, and unfortunately for him the name stuck.

When Fritz and I were about ten our favourite game

was to get into the Kirkpatricks' cellar through a loosened bar over the window and nick a few bottles. We always went for a mixed selection – champagne, red wine, white wine – and only ever took the stuff with plenty of dust on the bottle: obviously it wouldn't be missed if no one had bothered to drink it for thirty years. Having removed our booty, we'd sit in the big hedge behind the swimming-pool house and drink about a quarter of each bottle, chucking the rest away. It would be interesting one day to go back to that cellar and work out what we'd got through.

Despite his tender years, Fritz gave very good parties, which provided me with my one and only opportunity for adolescent snogging. One particularly good party was based on the theme 'Down in the Tube', and Fritz and I managed to persuade three girls to sneak with us into the drawing room (strictly forbidden territory) – where we took all our clothes off and we were rolling around on the floor in the dark when Fritz's grandfather, who was a bit short-sighted, switched the lights on, settled himself into a big armchair and proceeded to read the paper (mercifully a broadsheet). We made a hasty retreat.

Unfortunately my love life then entered a sexual and romantic wilderness for about the next ten years. It wasn't for lack of trying. I was mad about the daughter of one of our neighbours, and got very excited when I heard that she had given up ponies for boys. Sadly she didn't take me up, and the only possible oasis in the desert was Fritz's own girlfriend: I liked her and managed to get her in exchange for a friend of mine and a pair of skates, but it didn't work out.

Some boys' hormones start buzzing around a good

five years or so before others', and at Cothill we had just such a fellow. In racehorse terms, he would have been ready to run in a two-year-old race at Royal Ascot before most of his contemporaries had been broken in. Indeed, a measure of his precocity was that he was excused communal showers: he had been attracting a bigger crowd than Madame Tussaud's.

Freakish he may have been in the rate of his development, but he was a perfectly civil bloke, and one day offered to take me for a walk in the woods. This was totally out of bounds, but he was a prefect of the school, so I thought: Why not? It will be something to tell my mates about after lights out.

It was a beautiful summer's day, and we sat under the branches of a spreading oak tree and threw stones into the pond. Very idyllic – then suddenly he pulled his trousers down and asked me if I wanted to play with him. I took a look at the centre of all the attention – and thought, God knows what his mother has been feeding him.

I was off like a jack rabbit.

He caught up with me a couple of hours later and told me I would be expelled if I told anyone that we'd been out of bounds. So I didn't (until now).

One benefit which Cothill had for me was the transformation of a weakling recluse into a highly competitive sportsman. I became captain of the football team, in which role I was to experience the most euphoric moment of my sporting life. Never mind those Hennessys and Grand Nationals, the pinnacle was the day Cothill beat Summerfield 2–1. I was captain, I scored our two goals in the last four minutes when we looked headed for defeat, I got my school colours, and my father, who had come to watch the match, was so carried away by our victory that he bought the entire team Mars Bars after the game. I have never been so popular in my life.

During my time at Cothill my mother told me that my father had cancer. This was distressing news, but for me, unaware quite how ill he was, there was a very positive side to this situation: it meant that I was allowed home from school every weekend, thus invoking the jealousy of my schoolmates ('Why is Brooks allowed out?'). Although my mother encouraged me to spend as much time as I could with my father, who by then was confined to bed, I didn't realise just how serious his condition was, and I was keener on running around the farm or kicking a football against the wall.

I also had the distraction of the Common Entrance exam which would decide whether I would follow family tradition and go to Eton. Although I had never considered myself particularly gifted academically I can't have been quite as thick as I thought, as I ended up in the top twenty of those who sat that year's Common Entrance, and Eton, aware of my father's plight, marked my papers early so that he could know I'd succeeded in getting in.

They were only just quick enough.

One morning in the summer of 1977 the assistant headmaster of Cothill, Adrian Richardson, announced that he would like to see me in his study directly after lunch, and as I sloped along there I was desperately trying to work out what it was I'd done wrong: there was no other reason why he might wish to see me. After a timid knock on the door I was summoned in.

'Charles,' Richardson said immediately, 'I have some bad news for you. I'm afraid your father has died.'

For a moment I thought I must be hearing things. But Mr Richardson was continuing: 'Your friend Angela Bell will be here in ten minutes to pick you up and take you home.'

Among all the tears I can remember asking him questions which in retrospect seem extraordinary: 'Will things be different now? What will happen?' It felt like the end of my childhood.

(Twenty-one years later I went back to Cothill to celebrate my old maths master's eightieth birthday, and during the party I couldn't resist slipping out to find the study door behind which I had received the worst news of my life. I entered the room and shut the door after me, then closed my eyes and conjured up the image of a fourteen-year-old standing there sobbing. It was a weird experience.)

After my father's funeral I should have returned to Cothill for the remainder of the term but couldn't face it, and although my mother thought it would have been good for me to go back (she was probably right), she was very understanding and let me have my way.

Losing my father was a pretty shattering event, but I can't help but think that it was probably less complicated for me than for my brother and sister. Being the youngest, my relationship with him was perhaps less fully formed than theirs, and there were fewer hormones floating around my system. I have no doubt that the timing of this disastrous event contributed to both my brother and my sister subsequently becoming heroin addicts.

God knows how my mother got through all of this. I've always described myself as being bred 'out of a good tough hunting mare in the Cotswolds' – which is what my mother is. Her children have put her through some pretty high hoops, and she copes with it all. Her youngest being arrested by the Serious Crime Squad can't have been much fun (especially in view of the fact that she's been a magistrate for about twenty years), but Annabel's and Christopher's heroin addiction was a very different matter. Christopher showed no outward sign – when he placed himself into cold turkey on our farm nobody seemed to believe that he was a genuine heroin addict – but my sister, a more volatile character, made more noise about it. My mother had to charge down to London during my first weekend home from Eton because of one of Annabel's dramas: I could have killed her.

Through all this trauma, I never properly talked to my sister or brother about our father's death. Christopher didn't seem to want to discuss it at all and Annabel would just burst into tears, so I tended to steer clear of the subject. All three of us are quite obsessive characters, and it doesn't really surprise me that they got involved in drugs. But after a huge struggle they both came through it, and witnessing what happened to them taught me a lesson.

Both my father and grandfather had been to Eton, and Christopher was already there, four years ahead of me, when I arrived in the autumn of 1975. That year's entry turned out to be quite a horsy collection, as my contemporaries included David Loder, now a top trainer (we went to watch *International Velvet* together, and both fell deeply in love with Tatum O'Neal), Marcus Armytage, who would ride Mr Frisk to win the 1990 Grand National and is now a leading racing journalist, Luke Lillingston, today a top bloodstock agent, and Edward Benson, son of Charles Benson, formerly 'The Scout' on the *Daily Express*. Charlie Althorp, brother of Princess Diana, and Boris Johnson, now a well-known journalist, were in the year below, as was BBC racing correspondent Cornelius Lysaght.

And then there was Edgie. I'd known Charlie Egerton through hunting – his father Tom Egerton used to hunt with the Heythrop – and I think it's fair to say that after they made him they broke the mould. Imbued with the strength of his own convictions, he's never been one to feel himself hampered by convention – a characteristic which has made him one of the most talented jumps trainers of the present day – and this inclination to do his own thing goes right back to his childhood.

History relates how, when he was about nine, Edgie went missing the day he was due to be taken back to his prep school: he couldn't be found anywhere, and departure time was rapidly approaching, but the family cook thought she could flush him out of hiding. She baked one of his favourite chocolate cakes and placed it on a table in the middle of the lawn, and sure enough, after a short while there was a rustle in the bushes, followed by a blur as a figure dashed across the grass, grabbed the cake and headed for the shrubbery. But the gardener made a rapid interception and the quarry was caught. End of problem, they thought, as father and son drove off to school.

But while Captain Tom was having a quick drink with the headmaster and congratulating himself on delivering his wayward son safely back, our hero found an accomplice who helped him into the boot of the car, and home he went with his unwitting pater.

Edgie never did seem happy with the confines of school. One day at Eton when we were both about fourteen he sidled up to me in chapel.

'Brooks, you like racing, don't you? I'm going to Newbury this afternoon. Want to come?'

Apparently the great attraction of the afternoon's card was a horse named Snowtown Boy, trained by one Fred Winter, and although at this time my great sporting passion was football, I wasn't playing that day so agreed to go with him.

'Good. We'll meet at eleven.'

'*Eleven*?! I can't – I'll be in a lesson then.'

'Oh, never mind that – just don't turn up for it.'

And so we duly met at eleven. I was terrified of being caught sneaking out of school. Edgie was much more bold. Not only did he arrive at our rendezvous complete with trilby and binoculars, but he had a taxi waiting outside the school hall. His initial idea was that the taxi would take us to Slough station, from where we could get a train to Newbury, but once we were settled in the back he decided that it would be easier if the taxi took us all the way there: a fine idea, except for the fact that neither of us had any money. As luck would have it – and luck seemed to walk hand in hand with Edgie in those days – we arrived at the racecourse at the same time as his father, who was stewarding that afternoon.

'Hello, Charles; what are you doing here?'

'We've come to watch Snowtown Boy.'

'But I thought you were at school.'

'It's Saturday.'

'I thought we'd sent you to boarding school.'

Egerton senior duly paid off the taxi driver and – at Edgie's suggestion – gave us enough for a decent lunch and a bet.

That afternoon at Newbury gave me my first experience of the excitement of racing, and particularly of betting, and before long I was making a niche for myself as that vital cog in the mechanism of any well-oiled academic institution, the school bookmaker. The usual venue for betting was the school chapel, where bets would be scrawled on any available slip of paper and quietly passed to me along the pews. Once I'd consolidated all the day's bets I would phone my mother, who would then place them through her account with the local bookie in Chipping Norton. I can't have been a very intelligent bookmaker, as my schoolmates were betting with me tax-free and my mother would then have to pay the tax when laying the bets with her local man. In any event, my time as a bookie hit the rocks when I was cleaned out over a good horse of Robert Sangster's named Miners Lamp. One day all my clients were convinced that he'd win and lumped on. I was convinced that he wouldn't and stood the bets rather than passing them on through my mother. Miners Lamp won, and I was cleaned out. End of bookmaking career.

Naturally enough, Edgie had been one of my most enduring clients, but his attitude towards money was as unconventional as his attitude towards everything else. When he was about sixteen he was summoned to the manager's office of the bank in Eton High Street. After Edgie had plonked himself down in the most comfortable chair in the room, the manager came to the point.

'Mr Egerton. Do you realise that your overdraft is more than I earn in a year? What do you have to say about that?'

'I'd say that if I were you I'd get another job.'

Nor was hard graft really up Edgie's street. One afternoon there was a knock at the door of my study.

'All right, Brooks?'

'Yes. Want some tea?'

'No thanks. Any Scotch?'

'No. I've got a ginger beer if you'd like one.'

'No thanks. The fact is, I was wondering if I could borrow your Latin notes.'

'Of course, though don't copy them word for word – I'm not too hot at Latin.'

When the time came to hand in our work the following day Edgie had not returned my notes, and I was waiting nervously outside the classroom when suddenly, darting between the pillars of the cloister like J. P. R. Williams in full flight, along rushed C. R. Egerton. He sold me a dummy, swooped past me and deposited my notes in the master's tray without a word.

'Edgie! – what about my notes?'

'Oh, sorry, Brooks. I didn't have time to copy them' – so he'd tippexed out my name and substituted his own.

Sometimes I wonder how he became, and remains, one of my closest friends.

By mutual agreement with the school, Edgie took an early bath and went to a crammer in Oxford to try to get half-decent A-levels. Although his parents had always known that he was not short of ability, they were flabbergasted when his results came through. At last their boy had come good – three grades of 'Ab'.

Unbelievable. The celebrations were in full flow when some bastard pointed out that the exams had taken place during Royal Ascot, and 'Ab.' stood for 'Absent'.

A couple of days before the end of my fourth year at Eton, when I was sixteen, I heard a rumour that one of the school chaplains was about to leave. He was very popular with the boys, and I and a few other fellow conspirators thought he deserved a special send-off, so I sent round a note to a representative of each house telling them to bring along loo rolls to chapel the following morning. All duly obliged – though one house insisted on bringing those boxes of Bronco instead – and for my own contribution I donated about a hundred loo rolls, smuggled through in my trombone case. At a given signal we all fired off our ammunition in the direction of the departing chaplain; but then – to coin a phrase – the shit hit the fan something rotten. The whole of the year was summoned by the school headmaster Michael McCrum, and given the ultimatum: unless the ring-leaders own up, none of you will go home tomorrow. Two of us stood up and confessed, and for our honesty were rewarded with a date in the headmaster's study which could only mean one thing . . .

To be on the receiving end of a beating at Eton is not an experience I'd recommend to anyone. You kneel down at an ancient wooden block – doubtless a monument to the thousands who've been beaten there before, and it didn't do *them* any harm – and lean over the block to grasp a rail on the other side. From behind you comes the sound of the headmaster choosing the ideal weapon from a collection of eight or nine split canes – a bit like a golfer choosing his club – and then there's the horrible silence before the noise of his twenty-stride run-up along the wooden floor.

Thwack! The cane lashes you across the tops of your legs – protected only by one layer of thin pin-striped trousers – and every stroke leaves its mark.

After the first two I knelt upright to try to relieve the pain a little. 'Kneel still,' growled my attacker.

I had never felt pain like it, and was very bitter that my honesty at admitting what I'd done had been rewarded in this way. But I'll say one thing for beating: you never want to repeat the experience – the humiliation of which was multiplied several times over by having to shake McCrum's hand afterwards and thank him. That's tradition for you.

For my misguided attempt at giving the chaplain a jolly send-off I received six strokes – plus ten hours' detention for good measure. Lest I think I'd got off lightly, I was assured that I'd come within an ace of being expelled, and it was only because the incident was viewed as end-of-term high spirits that I'd be allowed to return.

So return I did, and in due course became rehabilitated – to the point where in my last year at the school I became part of the group of older boys known as 'Pop' whose task it was to patrol the pubs of Windsor and check that no boys from Eton were engaged in illicit drinking. To provide cover, we were allowed to consume half a pint of beer in each pub we visited. (The only boy I ever caught in six months' patrolling was the son of my housemaster, who was playing a fruit machine at Windsor Riverside station. The housemaster had been so unpleasant to me that 'busting' his son was a real result.)

It was on my way back to Eton from one of these patrols that I was accosted on the bridge in the middle of Windsor by a group of about six skinheads.

'You from the college?'

'No,' I said – but the tweed jacket and tie I was wearing must have been a dead giveaway, to say nothing of the accent.

'Looking for a fight?'

'Yes – if it's one against one' – but my offer did not go down well, and they all made for me at once, whisking me off my feet and hurling me through the plate-glass window of the nearby Elizabethan Tea Rooms. I was lying there dazed when the woman who ran the café, knowing trouble when she saw it, came out from behind the counter and started bashing me with a broom, then swept me out. The pub opposite gave me sanctuary until I was driven to Slough Hospital and treated in the casualty department. I still have the scars.

Although I had a constant problem with my house-master – which eventually got so bad that I moved out of his house to live with the school doctor – many of the other masters at Eton during my time were wonderful. There was, for instance, the occasion when a friend of mine sneaked off to Royal Ascot and had the misfortune to walk straight into his housemaster. Getting caught at Ascot was a sackable offence for the boy, but he had the presence of mind to hold out his hand and say, 'Hello, sir, you must be my twin brother Robert's housemaster. I've heard so much about you' – and then scarper.

That evening, as the housemaster went round the house, he sought out Robert.

'I met your twin brother at Royal Ascot today.'

'Oh really, sir? How was he?'

'Shut up, Robert – but if you should be speaking to him, do say that I never want to meet him there again.'

Then there was Martin Whiteley, who taught us divinity and who in his time had been a top-ranking three-day-eventer. Since he clearly knew about horses, on the morning of Derby Day 1981 I suggested to him that it would be more spiritually uplifting for me to watch Shergar at Epsom than attend his divinity class that afternoon.

'Absolutely not, Brooks. Be there or you'll be in trouble.'

Very unhappy at this lack of understanding, I turned up as ordered for the lesson – but just after three-thirty Moses was left to his own devices on Mount Sinai while Mr Whiteley produced a radio from under his desk – and we were able to hear Shergar and Walter Swinburn storming home by ten lengths.

For me, the best thing about Eton was the opportunity to play sport regularly, especially tennis. We had a pretty useful team and our own coach in Norwood Cripps, who had come to the school from Queens Club. He was very keen on racing, and on Irish Derby day that same year, well aware that I had had far more than I cared to lose on Lester Piggott and Shergar, he wound me up by telling me during our match that afternoon that the horse had got left in the stalls and taken no part in the race. In fact Shergar had won with incredible ease.

Our biggest problem on the tennis court used to be Christine St George, wife of the late Charles St George, who owned dozens of good racehorses such as Ardross.

Her son David was in the under-sixteen team, and the sight of his fantastically good-looking mother arriving to watch him play proved exceptionally distracting for the rest of us. Our tennis form took a dive on those occasions, even if our hormone levels didn't.

I played in the school football team at left back, and soccer facilities were so good that Graham Taylor used to bring his Watford team over to train at the school. This was the time of John Barnes and Luther Blissett, and the opportunity to see players of that quality at close quarters was invaluable. Much more comfortable on the sports field than in the classroom, I harboured half-serious notions of becoming a professional footballer, but Graham Taylor told me I was too small ever to make the grade as a goalkeeper. He was right, of course. I could stop shots but lack of height meant that I was undone by crosses, and after hearing the brutal truth from Graham I quietly abandoned any idea of earning my living at the game.

Whatever sport I was currently engaged in, I was always intensely competitive about it – a characteristic which goes right back to when I used to storm out of table tennis games against my elder brother once I started losing. By the age of sixteen I was becoming more serious about my riding, and started to ride in point-to-points. My mother was prepared to tolerate this, but only on condition that I prove to her that I was genuinely committed. Show that commitment, she said, and I'll buy you a horse.

Through family connections I had got to know trainer Toby Balding, and I spent the summer holiday in 1980 working at his stables in Hampshire. One of the country's leading trainers, Toby had nearly a hundred horses in the yard at the time, and a few weeks with him taught me an immense amount about the business of horses and racing.

When I arrived at Toby's, his wife Caro was about to depart for Scotland for a few weeks, and pointed out to me that my main duty would be to cook supper for him every evening. He liked his supper to be on the table by eight o'clock sharp, and she was leaving the deep-freeze stocked up with enough food to cover the period she'd be away. Cooking supper was not something I'd learned a great deal about at Eton but I was a reasonably dab hand in the kitchen, and on the first evening I duly prepared lamb chops, laid the table and knocked on the door of Toby's office.

'Supper is ready, Mr Balding!'

He opened the office door with a quizzical expression on his face.

'What did you say?'

'Mrs Balding said I was to cook you supper while she's away. It's on the table.'

'Don't be ridiculous!' he exploded. 'When she's away, we go out every night.'

So the lamb chops which I'd so dutifully and beautifully prepared were dumped in the bin, and off we went to the local pub.

There was a night-club at the nearby air base at Thruxton, and before our first foray up there Toby took my hand and wrote his telephone number on it.

'Why are you doing that?' I asked.

'If you get lucky, they'll know where to bring you back to.'

Fine, I thought, but what does 'get lucky' mean? That was another thing I hadn't learned at Eton.

At Toby Balding's, however, I learned a massive amount. I was far too inexperienced to be let loose looking after individual horses – Toby had some very high-class performers at that time, including the top-class hurdler Decent Fellow – but I rode out every day and mucked out enough boxes to give me a very solid grounding in the life of a racing stable. The following summer I spent at Newmarket with my mother's cousin Tom Jones, one of the great characters – as well as one of the best brains – among Flat trainers. Not only could he train horses of the calibre of Athens Wood and Touching Wood on the Flat and Tingle Creek over jumps, he also made himself something of a reputation as a poet:

THE TRAINER
OR, 'IT'S THE CREAKING GATE THAT GETS THE OIL'

'I envy the life of a trainer,'
Said a chap that I met on a plane:
'A lucrative life in the open,
'Surrounded by birds and champagne!

'High living at Ascot and Deauville
'At seasonal times of the year,
'Then home for a healthy old gallop –
'Why, it's life at ten thousand a year!'

Amazed at the stranger's delusions,
At a loss if to laugh or to cry,
I wondered if I should correct him,
And thought it at least worth a try.

'I fear, sir,' I said to the stranger,
'That you have been sadly misled.
'No trainer in England would ever
'Agree with a word you have said.'

The poem goes on to muse on the nature of owners –

'Peers, prostitutes, pansies and punters –
'Do they sound a pretty odd bunch?
'On the Turf they are prominent owners
'And we have the whole boiling to lunch!'

– and details the woes which await the trainer on his return to the yard after a day at the races:

'Your head man awaits your arrival.
'With relish he tells you the news:
'"The Travelling Man's broken his leg, sir,
'"The box driver's gone on the booze!

'"Bert's had a row at his digs, sir,
'"The new girl is pregnant, of course,
'"Sir Harry is coming round stables
'"There's ringworm all over his horse."'

'It's normal in other professions
'To prosper, retire and die,
'But trainers go on training horses
'I'm jiggered if I can think why.'

Our plane whispers down through the cloud base
(The temperature's ninety in Greece)
The stranger is standing me dinner,
And wants me to train for his 'niece'.

Despite all this work experience, I had no thought of working in racing when my education was over, and as the end of my time at Eton approached I had to think about university. My first target was Oxford, and having sat the entrance exam towards the end of 1981 I duly presented myself for interview at St Edmund Hall. I had been reliably informed that Teddy Hall had a particular liking for footballers, and while they might not be bowled over by my academic prowess I could well sneak in as a left back.

I arrived at the college the day before my interview, was put up in a student's room, and with time to kill went into the town and bought an Airfix kit of a Spitfire to make as a distraction before the ordeal the following morning. Having built the plane, I took it out into the corridor for its maiden flight. I checked that the coast was clear and launched the model into the air – at which point a man walked round the corner and found a Spitfire homing in on him. Having almost been pinned to the wall by this wayward flying object, he recovered his composure and, pausing only to ask, 'Are you all right, Mr Brooks?' proceeded on his way.

My bafflement as to how he knew my name was solved the next morning, when he turned out to be the very man who was interviewing me for my place at the college.

That was a bad start, but the interview got worse.

'I've been reading your housemaster's report,' he announced, 'and apparently you're only interested in horse racing.'

My housemaster at Eton and I did not get on at all, but still I had not expected to be the victim of such a negative report, and when I heard what he'd written I wished I'd saved myself the bother of swotting and sitting for Oxbridge after my A-levels.

Predictably Oxford declined the opportunity to have the pleasure of my company, and as I didn't want to go to any other British university I set my sights on the other side of the Atlantic. My first idea was to enrol at Wharton Hall in Pennsylvania for a business studies course – I'd heard that Wharton was as good as Harvard or Yale in that department – so I went over to see what could be arranged; but in the event I didn't manage to secure a place, so I moved on to New York, where I enrolled to major in business studies at NYU. It was so easy to get in that I thought there wouldn't be much point in going there, but returning from the States with a university place lined up for the following autumn at what sounded like a very respectable institution pacified my mother, who was beginning to worry about what turn my life might be taking.

Having left Eton at Christmas 1981, I had several months to fill before starting at NYU, and it was at this point that Edgie again played a pivotal role. He was planning to go and work with trainer Nick Gaselee in Lambourn, with whom he had spent some time the year before: would I join him? Having cut another deal with my mother, whereby she would tolerate my spending half my gap period in a racing stable on condition that I would spend the other half doing something more sensible, I was off with Edgie to Lambourn.

Nick had a yard of about forty horses at that time, which in Lambourn terms made it a middle-sized operation – ideal for enhancing my equine education. Edgie and I lived in the Egertons' house, were paid only the equivalent of our board and lodging, and had to learn from experience that stable staff put up with highly unsocial hours, starting work at six-thirty in the morning, carrying on until lunchtime, then having a couple of hours off in the afternoon before returning to duty for evening stables. In addition, we had to work every other Sunday. We may have been a couple of Old Etonian toffs, but we were learning the hard way, undertaking all the messiest jobs in the yard and putting up with any amount of stick from the other lads.

Nick had a wonderful head lad in the shape of 'Jumbo' Heaney, a great joker who dedicated himself to getting us fit. With the local postmistress Doreen he was always organising sports days and inter-yard competitions, and as a teacher he was perfect: he didn't come down on you too hard but he kept you up to your work, and the first lesson of stable management – that there has to be a degree of discipline – was soon learned.

Less easy to take was the way in which Nick's wife Judy tried to improve my table manners: I used to get a bollocking from her every morning for eating with my elbows on the table. By the time I came under Judy's watchful eye, though, it was too late: I've always eaten with my elbows on the table, and probably always will.

Nick himself was a gentleman and a great teacher: he had had the Prince of Wales under his wing when Prince Charles had made his high-profile but brief excursion into riding over fences the previous year. Legend has it that during that period Edgie was grooming his horse with his gloves on and Jumbo Heaney, walking past the box, noticed this.

'For fuck's sake, Charlie! Take your gloves off!', yelled

Jumbo – and then to his horror heard a mumbled 'Oohh aahh, sorry Jumbo' from the heir to the throne in the adjacent box.

I learned more in my first six months with Nick Gaselee than I did at any other period of my time in racing, and he was very influential in furthering my riding career.

Nick had found, in Northern Ireland, a horse named Gay Tab that I bought in partnership with my mother, and Gay Tab's role in life was to teach me to ride in races. Whether I would have had more fun drinking the best part of the Pipe of Croft '63 port which I had to sell to finance my half of the horse I've never quite decided.

The first time I rode him work he ran away with me on the gallops. Instead of pulling up after a mile and a half, as I was supposed to have him do, he simply kept going. Nick went apeshit, but the fact that the horse was capable of keeping going after galloping a stiff mile and a half obviously made a deep impression on the other lads in the yard. It was my own riding which made more of an impression on Jumbo Heaney, and on the way back to the yard he gave me an invaluable piece of advice about how to hold a horse pulling too hard: 'Imagine you're pulling the gardener off your mother.' (I often used to wonder whether Jumbo had given the same advice to the Prince of Wales.)

My first ride under Rules was at Nottingham in February 1982 in the Lancers Cup, a hunter-chase. The lads in the yard, mindful of what Gay Tab could do on the gallops and charitably forgetting what his rider could not do, lumped on the horse and were expecting to collect.

It all got a bit tight early on in the race, and I was taken aback to see two of the top amateur riders of the time, Oliver Sherwood and Jim Wilson, carving each other up on the third bend. I had read in the paper that Jim had been best man at Oliver's wedding, but such closeness counted for nothing in the heat of racecourse battle, and the language being exchanged between them was scandalous, even to my well-tempered ears. To my amazement the race started to go my way, and for the first time in my life I was in contention at the last fence, a situation I had never experienced in my point-to-point career. Unfortunately the rest of the race was summed up appropriately by the entry in the hunter-chasers' form book: 'Gay Tab – led last; hampered by rider on run-in'.

We were caught on the line and beaten a short head by Troyswood, ridden by Jim Wilson.

It was no disgrace to be beaten in a tight finish by Jim Wilson in your first ride under Rules – he was a highly accomplished 'professional' amateur who the previous season had won the Cheltenham Gold Cup, no less, on Little Owl – but I didn't see it that way. When I came into the unsaddling enclosure I was spitting mad. I refused to talk to anyone, and Judy Gaselee observed that if I was going to behave like a spoilt child I wouldn't be allowed to ride again. Back in the changing room I was still seething, and Tim Thomson Jones didn't help by pointing out: 'You're supposed to enjoy it.' What is the matter with these people? I thought: how could I enjoy getting beaten when I knew I should have won? My mother, who'd come up to Nottingham to watch the race, knew better than to say anything: she'd seen enough tennis racquets go out of the play pen over the years to know what a spoilt, bad-tempered bastard of a loser her son could be.

My own mood after the race was as nothing compared

with that of the lads back at the yard whose money had gone down the drain. I didn't exactly anticipate a hero's welcome on arrival the following day, but I naturally expected to be treated with the respect due to a jockey whose name had actually appeared in the morning papers. Unfortunately they saw things differently, and showed their view of my riding in the traditional manner. They stripped me naked in the tack room, sprayed my private parts with the purple iodine spray that you apply to a horse's cuts (which you can't get off for a month), covered the rest of me liberally with hoof oil, and chucked me into the muckhill. All rather unpleasant, but when I'd emerged and cleaned myself up I was told by one of the old hands that I'd got off quite lightly compared with one of my predecessors who had likewise incurred the lads' wrath: he had been purple-sprayed, then tied up in a haynet and suspended from a beam in the barn!

Despite the shortcomings of his regular pilot, Gay Tab became a pretty useful hunter-chaser, good enough to run in the Foxhunter Chase at the Cheltenham Festival in March 1982. But I gave him a real bollocks of a ride there, and we finished last of the nine who completed the course. Not surprisingly, Nick Gaselee wouldn't let me loose on anything else in the yard.

Edgie's own riding career had also got off to a slow start, probably made slower by our drinking into the early hours in the Red Lion in Lambourn the night before he was due to have his first ride under Rules at Southwell – a piece of irresponsibility which earned us both a huge bollocking from Nick Gaselee. 'Jockeys never go out the night before they ride,' he told us, but subsequent experience suggested he was not quite right. In any case, he had a point about Edgie, but why bollock me?

After six highly educational and enjoyable months – though no winners – it was time to take stock. There were no prospects of a position as assistant trainer at Nick Gaselee's and no vacancies for stable lads. Edgie decided to go to Australia to further his training education with the legendary Colin Hayes.

For my own part, I had heard of a possible vacancy closer at hand.

3

THE GUV'NOR

T HE SHAMBLING EIGHTEEN-YEAR-OLD dressed in his
father's ill-fitting suit – well, it was an important
interview – knocked on the door. A moment later it was
opened by a short, strong figure with piercing eyes.

'Mr Winter?'

He spoke gruffly: 'Yes. What do you want?'

'Charlie Brooks, sir. I wrote to you. I was wondering
whether you needed a pupil assistant trainer.'

'How much experience have you got?'

I told him of my six months with Nick Gaselee and how
I'd ridden in a few point-to-points and hunter-chases.

It didn't take a man of Fred Winter's insight long to
work out that I wasn't going to be a great deal of use
to him, but I persevered, adding that I hoped to ride
in races as well as learn the finer points of training.
On hearing this, he promptly put one hand around my
wrist and delivered his verdict: 'Forget it – you're going
to be far too heavy. You're too inexperienced. You'd

be better off doing something else. Have you got any qualifications?'

'Fourteen O-levels and three A-levels.'

'So what do you want to come here for? Get yourself a proper job.'

End of interview. So he thought.

I had heard that Mark Wilkinson, then Fred Winter's pupil assistant, was leaving Uplands. The position of pupil assistant in a racing yard offers the opportunity to learn the ropes of racehorse training at the hands of an experienced professional (though for little or no pay), and my first thought was that this made a suitable vacancy for me, a good move after my short time with Nick Gaselee. My second thought was that there was no way I'd ever get a job with Fred Winter.

Then coincidence stepped in. I was on holiday in Ibiza with Michael and Angela Bell, who farmed next door to us in Oxfordshire, and on the beach I bumped into Fred Winter's daughter Jo. Rather embarrassed to raise the subject, I mentioned how I was thinking of getting in touch with her father about the job but was too pessimistic to have written to the great man. Maybe you should, she said, so I did – with the result that one morning in September 1983 I found myself knocking timidly on the side door of the Winter house at Uplands.

Like most people connected with racing, I'd been in awe of Fred Winter for as long as I could remember. As a jockey he had become one of the all-time heroes of the sport, famed for his strength, determination and horsemanship, and as a trainer was held in awe throughout Lambourn – and well beyond – for the no-nonsense discipline with which he ruled his yard. By the time of my approach to him the stars who had inhabited the famous 'Millionaires' Row' of boxes at Uplands in the 1970s – Lanzarote, Crisp, Pendil, Bula, Killiney and Midnight Court – were just glorious memories; even remoter memories were Jay Trump and Anglo, the pair of Grand National winners he had sent out in his first two seasons' training. As a rider his record had been extraordinary: champion jockey four times, with two Grand Nationals (Sundew and Kilmore), two Cheltenham Gold Cups (Saffron Tartan and Mandarin) and three Champion Hurdles (Clair Soleil, Fare Time and Eborneezer) to his credit. He was one of the very few jockeys to have won the Champion Hurdle and Cheltenham Gold Cup in the same year, and the only man in the history of jump racing to have both ridden and trained winners of Grand National, Gold Cup and Champion Hurdle. For all that, his most famous moment remained his ride on Mandarin in 1962, when he steered the horse to a short-head victory in the Grand Steeplechase de Paris after the bit had snapped early in the race and the horse had broken down in the closing stages.

That Fred Winter was a racing legend was not up for debate. So to say that I was awestruck to be knocking on that back door is understating the case: I was terrified. This, after all, was a sacred place in National Hunt racing, the holy of holies.

But at least I was on time. 'Whatever you do,' Jo Winter had advised me, 'don't be late.' (My own later acquaintance with the Guv'nor's attitude to punctuality underlined the wisdom of this advice. He was fanatical about timekeeping. Once when we were due to go racing at Sandown Park together I drove into the yard about half a minute late for a lift, just as he was driving out: he wouldn't wait, and I had to follow him all the way there.)

For that first encounter I had not been late, but the great man had clearly been unimpressed, both by the suit and by the figure inside it. 'Get yourself a proper job' had clearly been his idea of the termination of our interview; but it was not mine. I was desperate to work for him, and I had to persist. 'How about my being a stable lad? Have you got any vacancies for stable lads?'

He thought for a moment, then asked me to wait there while he went to find the head lad Brian Delaney, who was responsible for hiring and firing. Later I came to realise that the last thing Brian would have wanted was an Old Etonian with a Hooray Henry accent making a nuisance of himself in the yard by trying to be a stable lad, but as luck would have it he was at that moment riding out with second lot and not available to offer what would no doubt have been a highly individual view of my prospects. Frustrated in his search for Brian, Fred Winter came back and grunted: 'Start on Monday'. I was in.

I returned to my mother's house in a state of great excitement, dampened on arrival by her reaction. She had put me through an expensive education with the idea that it might prepare me for a serious career – in the City perhaps, or the army. Certainly a future as a stable lad had not figured in her plans for me, and she was less than impressed by the news that I intended to pursue this whim of working in racing.

Then there was the small matter of that place at New York University.

My mother's objections fell on deaf ears. NYU would have to go by the board, though in the circumstances I don't suppose they missed me too much. I was fired up by the prospect of working for Fred Winter and would not be persuaded out of it, and on the Monday, bang on time at six-thirty a.m., I duly turned up for my first day's work at Uplands.

There was no gentle breaking in of the raw recruit – rather a dive straight into the deep end. First lot on my first day I was put up on a horse named Colonial Lad, owned by the indefatigable Duke of Albuquerque, famous for his devil-may-care attempts at getting round in the Grand National. We did one canter up the all-weather gallop, and Colonial Lad pulled my arms out: I couldn't ride one side of him, and it was only my fear of getting the sack on day one that kept our partnership intact. But I survived, and slowly – very slowly – settled into the routine of one of the great training yards in the land.

In my early years Fred Winter himself remained very much in the background: during my first months I hardly had any contact with the Guv'nor beyond the occasional 'Good morning, sir' and reporting to him how a horse had worked as we walked home from the gallops.

Head lad Brian Delaney, on the other hand, was a more immediate source of terror.

Brian had been with Fred from the beginning of his training career, and had long been the linchpin of the whole Uplands operation. He had started in racing with the famous Flat trainer Jeremy Tree (for whom he had one ride as an apprentice) before moving to the National Hunt scene, and over jumps had ridden three winners, each time beating the great Stan Mellor into second: it was part of the tradition of Uplands that every new recruit to the yard had to have his ear bent about how the head lad had put that Stan Mellor in his place!

From the start, the bollocking from Brian Delaney was an essential part of the routine. Every single week there would be something – something not done right, or not done at all – which would trigger the mother and father of a dressing-down. The cause did not have to be very dramatic – failure to grease a horse's feet, not brushing him over properly after riding out – but the bawling out was inevitable. Never Deemed, one of my first pair of horses, had very manky skin, and when clipped out in the winter always looked as if he hadn't been groomed for weeks; so I'd be bollocked because the horse did not look better. (And it wasn't only the look of horses that Brian was fastidious about. He told me years later that his first ever impression of me was my individual dress sense – odd socks and shirt tail hanging out!)

The fact was that Brian Delaney had little time for amateurs, and certainly didn't want some posh would-be amateur rider messing about the yard as a stable lad. It was a bit like going through Sandhurst and suffering at the hands of an abrasive sergeant-major. I had a pretty hard time of it, but it knocked the edges off me, and made me think that every precious little Old Etonian would benefit from a stint as a stable lad. The rest of the lads were hardly a source of comfort, and my mother's guarded response to my joining the yard was positively tropical compared with the reaction I got from my fellow workers. At first they simply didn't talk to me at all – presumably they had me marked down as a stuck-up toff – and it was months before I even started to become accepted.

The early-morning routine for a lad at Uplands was simple.

Arrive at six-thirty a.m. Muck out your two horses, and usually one other to cover for a lad away racing.

My first two charges, Never Deemed and Joe Sunlight, were acknowledged to be a pair of the stable's lesser lights. When Joe Sunlight ran in a novice hurdle at Sandown Park I told his jockey John Francome that the horse was in good form and could win. John, in his inimitable style, pronounced that 'This fucking thing couldn't win if he started yesterday!' But he did, and as I led 'Joey' triumphantly into the winner's enclosure Fred came striding up to greet us with a huge smile. 'Unbelievable,' he said. 'You're a genius!' As it happened, I did think I'd done rather well with the horse: I'd ridden him in all his work and I loved him to bits. So in reply to this accolade from the Guv'nor I offered a modest little 'Thank you,' to which he retorted: 'Not you, you bloody idiot. I was talking to John!'

Fill the water bucket, get a fresh bale of straw outside the stable door, with fresh hay on top of it, tack up the horse you're riding first lot and be ready to pull out by seven forty-five. Then ride out until about nine, come back in, take half an hour for breakfast.

I often used to have my breakfast with an old lad called Harry Foster in the lower of Uplands' two tack rooms. Harry did some good horses in his time, the best of which was Lanzarote, the winner of the 1974 Champion

Hurdle who was tragically killed in the Cheltenham Gold Cup three years later. He used to give me a bit of sandwich for breakfast which was always a cold greasy fried egg between two bits of bread – apart from one morning when his wife put the rent book in the sandwich instead of the egg. He probably wasn't the best of husbands, but he was a good client of Ladbrokes.

In my day Harry did two good horses, Observe (whom I would come to know better) and Al Kuwait, and one day decided to have a serious punt on Al Kuwait at Cheltenham. John Francome rode, got interfered with very badly and was beaten in a race he should have won. When John came in he said that the other jockeys needed riding lessons. 'Fuck my luck, boy! Fuck my luck, boy!' Harry reported to me indignantly the following morning. 'All he could talk about was riding lessons.'

On a much earlier occasion, before I arrived at the yard, Harry had taken charge of a French horse called Beau Champ – the second word in French pronounced with a soft 'ch' and no 'p', sort of '-shom', but by Harry with a hard 'ch' and hard 'p': '-champ'. One day when this horse ran, Harry thought that Beau Champ was a good thing. There was a big crowd and no closed circuit TV in those days so the diminutive Harry could see nothing as the commentator in his best French accent called home Beau Champ (with a soft 'ch' and no 'p') a convincing winner. Dismayed, Harry turned to the travelling head lad: 'Fuck my luck, boy! Fuck my luck, boy! Mine was never mentioned!'

He probably had a few punters to whom he passed information, but he didn't expect that they'd benefited much from it: 'My punters are always skint, boy, always skint!' was one of his constant refrains.

Lads like Harry Foster were the salt of the earth in Lambourn stables in those days, but he could see that times were changing, and didn't like it one bit: he was always complaining that whereas in the old days all the talk in the yard was about horses, now it was 'Sex and football, boy, sex and football.' Mind you, he wasn't one to talk.

After breakfast we'd ride out second – and sometimes third – lot, which could cover a variety of activities, from walking the horses around the roads to galloping them on the days of serious work.

Despite those weekly bollockings and the initial hostility of the other lads, there was no questioning that Uplands was a magical place to work, and no doubt that we all knew we were part of something very special. Within Lambourn's training community Uplands was considered arrogant and superior, and that suited us fine. There was one strip of gallop up on Mandown, now known as the 'Cheltenham strip' (where Cheltenham Festival-bound horses work) which we referred to as 'our strip', a piece of land so exclusive that only Uplands horses would work there. Rivalry with Fulke Walwyn's almost equally legendary yard next door – 'over the wall', we called it – was huge.

Our arrogance was rooted in the incontestable fact that we had better horses – and, in the footballing term, more strength in depth – than anywhere else in the village. Not that all the horses were top-class, of course; and in my early days I had to team up with some of the yard's distinctly less illustrious inhabitants.

One such was Fionnadoir, a horse bought by a group of people including my mother, who thought that having an interest in a horse in the yard would afford her son at least the occasional race-riding opportunity. Fionnadoir was – not to mince words – a complete headbanger, and taking him out quietly on his own was the only way to train him. If he saw an open space he'd bolt, so Nicky Henderson (who had been Fred's assistant but was now training in his own right) would let me take the horse to the enclosed paddock at Windsor House and canter him round and round and round.

On one occasion when I was away from the yard, Fionnadoir was ridden out by a lad named Paul Simpson, universally known as 'Simmo'. Doubtless the other lads thought that the horse was only so wayward because he was ridden by that arsehole Brooks, and a better rider would be able to control him properly. Fionnadoir and Simmo were walking along the foot of one of the gallops, passing behind a row of fir trees which had been roped off to show the way out, when the horse began to get more and more agitated.

'What that horse needs is a crack round the arse,' advised one of the other lads, no doubt mindful of the fact that his regular rider – me – would have been far too scared to do anything of the sort. So Simmo gave him one – and the next thing the other lads saw was Fionnadoir crashing through the row of firs, rope and branches wrapped around his neck, heading off over the horizon with Simmo clinging on grimly. They did not screech to a halt until they reached the yard. No lasting harm was done, but the other lads had a little more respect for me after they saw what a true nutcase that horse was.

Trying to control Fionnadoir at home was one thing. In public, he could be a positive embarrassment. One day when I was riding him at Sandown he got very fractious leaving the paddock, scraped Ray Warren, our horsebox driver who was leading him up, against the wall by the Rhododendron Walk which leads to the course, then cantered across the tarmac towards the glass doors which lead into the stand, with me incapable of steering him on to a more orthodox course. Once I got down to the start John Francome, who was riding another horse in the race, had to grab hold of one of my reins and lead Fionnadoir round like an adult guiding a child on his pony. Another time, before the start of a race at Devon and Exeter, he tried his usual trick of throwing his head back and then lunging forward, and managed to bring his forelegs down on the bonnet of a car – with his hind legs the other side of the rail, me still sitting on top, and Ray hanging on for dear life.

Such indignities were not exactly what I'd had in mind when contemplating the development of my riding career. But I was probably alone in thinking of my having any sort of riding career: the idea of my taking part regularly in races was certainly not a thought which preoccupied Fred Winter or anyone else in the yard. Oliver Sherwood, assistant trainer, was stable amateur, and even were he not available the idea of putting up C. P. E. Brooks was simply not on the agenda. At that stage my riding was very much a source of amusement (as in some quarters it remained), and I was not exactly a budding J. Francome.

That first season as a stable lad sped by, and at the end of it I was more convinced than ever that I wanted to stay in racing, despite the continuing objections of my mother, who clung to the idea that there were more appropriate futures for me than a lifetime as a stable lad. But I was very enthusiastic about riding, and the more experience I got at Uplands the keener I became on trying my luck as an amateur jockey.

Nurturing an ambition to ride in races was one thing. Achieving it was not so simple. I took to riding out for a few small trainers in Lambourn outside working hours at Uplands, and that way began to pick up rides in races. The horses I rode were pretty bad, but it was a start, and for a period I was getting very few rides for Fred Winter but the occasional one for other people, in point-to-points as well as under Rules.

As far as Fred Winter himself was concerned, working for a riding legend did not necessarily mean constantly receiving insights and tuition. For him, the situation was quite straightforward. If you asked for advice, he would give it; if not, he would not volunteer it. Fred tended to take the view that if a jockey makes a horlicks of a race, if he's any good he'll know he screwed it up, and if he's not any good there's no point wasting breath telling him where he went wrong. But if you kept asking him he'd keep telling you. He seemed to appreciate that I would always try my best, and he always wanted to reward hard work. But he was too frightening to be a natural teacher, and never more so than when we were schooling a horse over fences or hurdles. The atmosphere was tense and the air blue as he yelled out his instructions and dispensed ripe bollockings to all and sundry: if you got away without an earful you were having a good morning.

At the end of my first year I asked the Guv'nor if I could return the following season, and – after a pause slightly too long for my liking – he said that I could.

Needing a roof over my head during my first year at Uplands, I moved into a cottage in East Garston with Mark Bradstock, then a lad at Fulke Walwyn's yard, later assistant to that great man and now a trainer in his own right. I'd known Mark a little before I moved in with him, but I was not prepared for his obsessive tidiness, which at first I thought would drive me mad. Everything had to be in exactly the right place. He went to bed very early, which was not my way, and seemed to have a very serious attitude about most things – again a contrast with myself.

He'd loosen up occasionally, though, and when we heard that it was being put about by the villagers of East Garston that we were a couple of gays shacked up together, we thought we'd play up to this. When we went to do our shopping in the village store I waited until there was a good complement of old ladies in the shop, then loudly requested of Chris behind the counter: 'Could I have a big pot of Vaseline, please? – No, not that small pot, I need a big pot.' Having made my purchase I minced out of the shop, calling 'Don't be long, darling!' to a blushing Bradstock as he faced the shocked gaze of the villagers.

But our cover was soon broken.

Sara Lawrence, daughter of Lord Oaksey, was a great friend of mine. She was living in the village with her grandmother and I felt she might benefit from some younger company, so I asked Mark if she could come round to tea one day. He did not much like the disruption of a visitor but grudgingly agreed, suggesting that she didn't stay too long.

Talk about chemistry between two people. Sara arrived for tea. I left them to it at nine-thirty, and didn't see either of them again for four weeks. She never left, and now they've been married for ages and have two children.

Mark and I had our moments. At the Cheltenham Festival one year we were queuing for a hamburger when our attention was taken by the woman in front of us. She was well short of getting her bus pass, but the years had not been kind to her. She was dressed in high heels that she had scarcely learned to walk in, a very brief, tight mini-skirt and a waist-length fur jacket, the whole effect set off by bright red lipstick that looked as if it had been applied with a large paintbrush. Mark pointed surreptitiously at her and gave me a wink – at which he received a hefty thwack on his back from a large hairy fellow sporting various tattoos on his arms: 'Oi, you two! Keep your eyes off what you can't afford!'

Suitably chastened, we left Cheltenham and went out to dinner in Hungerford. During the evening I started complaining of a terrible stomach ache, to which Mark's response was that I should stop whining and drink some sherry – 'That'll put you right.' But the pain persisted, and after I had been lying under the table for an hour the lady who owned the restaurant, obviously thinking that the moaning was putting off her other customers, decided to call a doctor – despite Mark's insisting to her that there was no need to bother. The doctor duly arrived and he and Mark took me upstairs to examine me: he felt my stomach and asked me to drop my trousers, then put on a rubber glove, at which point

Mark was overcome by such a fit of laughter that the doctor asked him to leave.

After having a good feel with the rubber glove, the doctor gave his opinion that my appendix was about to rupture and I should be got to hospital as soon as possible. An ambulance was summoned and I was duly stretchered off and loaded in – then off we sped, sirens blaring, towards Battle Hospital in Reading. As we joined the M4 the ambulance bounced over a ramp in the road and I was hit by a terrible pain, followed by a considerable expulsion of gas – after which I felt fine.

I knocked on the window to alert the ambulance driver to this change in the situation.

'My pain's gone' – I was too embarrassed to tell him about the wind – 'Don't rush on my part. Er, any chance of dropping me off at home?'

'Lie down,' I was told. 'The pain always goes as the appendix is bursting.'

I did as I was told, and as soon as we reached the hospital was rushed into X-ray.

'Look,' I pleaded, 'if you've got any serious casualties here please deal with them before me,' but they carried on pondering my case, scratching their heads at the X-rays then deciding to keep me in for observation.

What a night! The poor woman in the bed next to me was passing a kidney stone, and I got little rest. The following morning I phoned my mother.

'Can you come and visit me?'

'No. I'm going hunting.'

'But I may need a lift home.'

'Catch the bus.'

And I hadn't even told her about the wind . . .

After two nights in hospital I had recovered sufficiently from the excesses of the Cheltenham Festival to discharge myself.

After a couple of years with Mark (and, latterly, Sara) I decided it was time to buy my own bricks and mortar, so I bought a sweet-looking cottage from Malcolm Bastard, who had ridden many winners for Fred Winter. What looked like a cosy, snug thatched cottage in the summer showed its true colours in the winter, when without central heating it was cold and damp, the freezing air whistling through the metal window-frames. It was also only one room wide, which meant that with so many outside walls the temperature rapidly plummeted. In fact there was very little comfort about it at all, and it was highly unpopular with the fairer sex.

An additional problem was that I was madly in love with one of my lodgers; she did not return the feeling, but just in case she might be persuaded one day to change her opinion, I didn't want to queer my pitch by appearing at the cottage after dark with other girls, who in any case didn't fancy the discomforts of the place. So I had to be careful whom I brought back; but on the other hand I had no intention of living like a monk, and luckily the solution was staring me in the face – well, a hundred yards down the road.

Mark and Sara were very sound sleepers and always went to bed early, which in the winter meant that as often as not they'd leave the embers of a good fire glowing in the hearth – and on good evenings they'd leave the remains of supper out. I knew where they hid the key to their back door and had become a close personal friend of their lurcher Crumble, so getting into their cottage was easy. Whenever my offers to 'come back and look at my stamp collection' were accepted towards the end of an evening I would take my new friend back not to the chilly wastes of my own cottage, but to Bradstock's nice warm fireside – where we'd have a quick snack and a drink and settle down to watch those embers and let nature take its course.

This worked without complication on about a dozen occasions. My guest didn't know it wasn't my house, and Bradstock was none the wiser. But unfortunately my luck ran out one evening after a couple of months of this scam when Mark came downstairs to get some cough mixture. We were in an advanced state of undress, but Mark was very cool about it: as he stepped over us he just glanced at me and muttered, 'You're unbelievable.'

Luckily he didn't hang around for a prolonged conversation, and I was able to reassure my fellow philatelist, 'It's all right – he's just the lodger.'

After that encounter the object of my unrequited love back in my own cottage went to Australia, so I decided to splash out on central heating and double glazing, and concentrate on playing at home.

Individual pursuits apart, there was plenty of fun to be had around Lambourn in those days, and from the vantage point of extreme middle age it does strike me that life for the younger elements of the racing profession in that area has become progressively less jolly and more serious.

In the 1980s Jenny Pitman's garden gnomes used to be regularly kidnapped after a good evening out. Quite understandably, she did not find this as hilarious as everyone else did, but it became a Lambourn tradition.

After each kidnapping the ransom notes would be sent, and then the gnomes would appear in the most unusual places – such as on markers halfway up the gallops.

One Sunday night Tim Thomson Jones, Simon Sherwood and Jimmy Duggan (who had just started to ride for Fred) were summoned by Mrs P to Weathercock House where apologies were demanded for the latest kidnap. Simon sportingly carried a tape recorder in his pocket to preserve this historic moment for posterity, which is how we know that Mrs Pitman, having lined them up with their hands behind their backs like naughty schoolboys, gave them a right dressing-down.

To Tim: 'I would have expected it of you.'

To Simon: 'I wouldn't have expected it of you.'

And to Jimmy: 'And who the fuck are you?'

She'd know before long that Jimmy was a very fine rider who, like so many others, never really got the opportunities he deserved to show just how good he could be.

Jimmy was also fearless, as was apparent the day he went to London with his brother and his little terrier Alfie, who was Jimmy's best friend in the world. They were on the Underground, and when their stop arrived the two brothers got off and started walking along the platform, each thinking the other had Alfie – then suddenly realised, to their horror, that the dog was still on the train, now moving away and picking up speed. Quick as a flash, Jimmy leaped on to the back of the last carriage and clung there for dear life until the tube arrived in the next station, where he got down and rushed along to retrieve Alfie. What a star!

Even in our day we felt we weren't having quite as

much fun as our predecessors; but there was one bunch who managed to have more fun probably than the rest of us put together. This was the Brat Pack, the nucleus of which lived out at Ashdown, a couple of miles from Lambourn, and consisted of Eddie Hales, John Durkan, Henry Daly and Ed Dunlop, with Jamie Osborne never far away. Their devotion to fun did not prevent each from becoming very successful in his chosen area. Eddie Hales is a successful producer of horses in Ireland, Henry Daly and Ed Dunlop are among the brightest prospects of the younger generation of trainers, while Jamie was a top-class jockey and is about to make a great impact as a trainer on the Flat.

John Durkan's death from leukaemia in October 1998 was a shattering experience for all who knew him. He came to work for me at Uplands when he came over from Ireland, and was hugely popular in the yard from day one. He was very funny and had a great turn of phrase – 'Women shouldn't be allowed near horses or cars' was one of his more contentious offerings – and moreover was the only amateur rider I've known to whom Brian Deláney took straight away. John rode a good few winners for us before he heard that Oliver Sherwood was looking for an assistant and decided to move on. I really missed him: sitting in the office after evening stables having a drink with JD – discussing problems, plotting future plans for the horses – is my fondest memory of my whole time training horses. From Oliver's he went on to work for John Gosden at Newmarket, where he spotted the hurdling potential of Istabraq: he recommended the horse to his father-in-law Timmy Hyde as a purchase for J. P. McManus, and would have ended up training that great hurdler himself had his illness not intervened.

Although there was not a position at Uplands which could have tempted him to stay – Jo Winter was my assistant at the time – I was very upset when he left. This was a childish reaction on my part, as I would have done the same as him in his situation, but for a while we were scarcely on speaking terms. The rift was eventually healed, and I can recall the relief I think we both felt when we sat down in a quiet corner at Newmarket during the Guineas meeting and talked properly to each other for the first time in years. All the problems between us were soon water under the bridge.

His death was a big loss. I still have a picture of him on my office desk, and can't ever look at it without bringing back to mind the antics in which he used to get involved.

One spring when the Brat Pack was getting seriously above itself, Jeremy and Lucinda Graham (with whom I was living as a lodger in Eastbury) and I decided to give them a little surprise. The Swan at Great Shefford was very much the 'in' pub of the area in those days (I once watched the great fast bowler Bob Willis drink a pint of kümmel in about five minutes there), and one evening was the venue for a big birthday party to which the Brat Pack had been invited. We hid in a barn near their cottage until they left for the party, then crept out and went into the house (no locked doors in those days) with fifty chickens we'd bought for the purpose in Reading, distributed said chickens around every room in the place, then made our own way to the party at The Swan.

We had tipped off the landlord Mike Lovett (a man who knew the meaning of fun) to throw the Brat Pack out at midnight on the dot, and as soon as they were out of the pub we ran across the fields to get into position to witness their homecoming. Unfortunately we forgot that one of these fields was protected by electric sheep fencing, which as luck would have it happened to be on. It felled us like a tripwire, one of our number getting a good blast of current, another ending up with a cracked rib. So it was a depleted party who crouched in the dark outside the Brat Pack's cottage to witness their welcoming by their unexpected house guests, and they were not impressed. Total sense of humour failure followed, so we beat a retreat and left them to clear up the mess.

The camaraderie which bound the Brat Pack together was called upon by Jamie Osborne after a particularly bad fall at Worcester had put him flat on his back and immobile in the Nuffield Hospital in Oxford.

His mother, concerned at her dear son's indisposition, came down from Yorkshire to visit him in hospital and announced that she'd go and spring clean his house for him while he was out of action.

'No, Mum, you don't have to do that.'

'I know what you're like. I bet your bedroom's in a right state. I'll come and visit you again tomorrow . . .'

Now this was by no means music to our broken-up jockey's ears. In fact it was potentially disastrous, and there was only one thing for it: get on the phone to Eddie Hales.

'Hales! Get round to my house now and get rid of those magazines under my bed. You'll have to break in round the back . . .'

The next day, flushed from a hard morning's spring cleaning, Mrs Osborne returned to the Nuffield: 'You don't change, Jamie, do you? I know how you like your breakfast in bed – but fancy keeping the marmalade under it.'

If I spent most of my first year with Fred Winter as an awestruck innocent deeply grateful for the privilege of being associated with such a legendary yard, that feeling was beginning to wear off as the second year progressed, and I was starting to become a little disenchanted. My riding career had not exactly taken off, and I was wondering what the future held.

In May 1985, towards the end of the jumps season, I was riding back from first lot on Mandown, above Lambourn, when the Guv'nor came upsides.

'Well,' he said in a tone I had not often heard from him, 'what are you planning to do with the rest of your life?'

I told him I was probably going to go and work in the City – an ambition my mother still nourished for me, and one she was sure I'd pursue once I'd got this racing bug out of my blood.

'Good idea,' muttered Fred, and rode on.

Later that morning I was mowing the lawn outside the Winters' house – a regular chore for a lad – when I saw Fred leave the house and come towards me. He was extremely particular about how the grass should be cut, and I started to prepare myself for another bollocking.

'Turn it off!' he rasped, and when I had done so he dropped the bombshell: 'Oliver Sherwood is going to start training next season. Do you want the job of assistant trainer? I'll give you a couple of days to think about it.'

'I don't need a couple of days. I'll accept!'

I knew that I was considered very young – I was only twenty-two – and very raw, and I had no idea why I'd been singled out in this way, though I suspect that Fred, encouraged by Di and his daughters, had decided that in me at least they would be getting the devil they knew.

(I later learned that Fred had gone back in for breakfast after first lot to be quizzed by Di: 'Did you offer him the job?' 'No. I just asked him what he planned to do and he said he was going to work in the City, so I left it at that.' 'Don't you think you'd better offer him the job and see how he reacts?' Hence Fred's coming out of the house for a second try.)

To be offered the position as assistant to Fred Winter, at the time the current champion trainer over jumps, was the racing equivalent of being offered the job as assistant to the head of ICI. And yet, though I knew it would be great experience and a very good entry on my CV, it still did not really occur to me that I wanted to make a career as a racehorse trainer. The other lads at Uplands would doubtless have agreed with me – and they were staggered that I'd landed the job.

Working directly under Fred was a highly character-forming experience. He didn't mind people making mistakes so long as they didn't make the same one twice, and if you did make a mistake you faced the consequences. On one occasion I forgot to declare the blinkers in which a horse was due to run so he had to take part without them – and Fred insisted that I go to the course and admit my error to the owners.

In those days the system of entries was far more convoluted than today's streamlined five-day system.

Race conditions were published in the *Racing Calendar*, and entries had to be sent to Weatherbys three weeks in advance, on one designated day of the week. At Uplands it was the task of the assistant trainer to make pencil annotations in the programme book indicating which horse in the yard might be entered for a particular race (depending on that race's conditions, the state of fitness of the horse, and so on), and take the book – rather like handing in a school exam – to the master to be scrutinised: Fred would then delete ones he didn't like and add ones I'd missed. Within a couple of years I could so nearly second-guess what Fred was thinking that he made very few amendments to my suggested entries, but this was a crucial area of my responsibilities, and a mistake could be disastrous.

Back then you had to cancel declarations (rather than declare a horse to run) and one day I forgot to cancel the engagements for several horses at Ascot. The horses were duly withdrawn, but the stable was heavily fined for this oversight – and I foolishly offered to pay the fine. Fred, knowing when a lesson was there to be taught, accepted my offer. This I thought a little stern, as during my time as assistant I continued to be paid a stable lad's wage, topped up with a bonus for each winner the yard sent out.

The daily routine was straightforward. At six-thirty in the morning I'd collect the papers from the village and take them up to the yard, arriving by six forty-five. In the kitchen, Fred would always be emptying the washing-up machine and squeezing a glass of fresh orange juice for his wife Di while waiting for the kettle to boil. Fred was invariably grumpy before breakfast, and any form of small talk was best avoided. So it was straight down to work: he had prepared the list of horses who were due to school – that is, have jumping practice over hurdles or fences – that day, and I'd take it out to the head lad so that riding arrangements could be made.

I would then tack up the horses which the Guv'nor and I would be riding out first lot. Many trainers ride a hack – often a retired racehorse – to accompany their string up to the gallops, but Fred always used a horse currently in training, and even well into his sixties would display the incredible strength which had made him such a great jockey. He'd never school a horse himself, but was happy to ride work on one, sitting bolt upright with his hands clamped down: not a horse in the yard could get the better of him, however hard it pulled.

To work so closely with Fred after having known him only as a very remote figure when I was a stable lad was initially a frightening experience. Quite apart from his pre-breakfast grumpiness, which everyone in the yard had to accept, he could be quite abrupt. He liked everything to be done just so, and was, not surprisingly, very set in his ways.

First lot went out at around seven forty-five, by which time it was beginning to get light in midwinter. The daily routine for each horse naturally varied according to the individual, his fitness and the proximity of the next race. Different trainers had different preferences, but in those days a typical routine for a horse at Uplands might be:

Monday: long trot
Tuesday: light canter uphill
Wednesday: walk

Thursday: more taxing canter uphill, a mile or so
Friday: trot
Saturday: work round 'the bowl' and up the hill
Sunday: stay in box

Interspersed with that routine was schooling over fences or hurdles. 'Work mornings', when selected horses would be asked to have a serious gallop, would always be Tuesday and Saturday. The day before a race a horse would have a good 'pipe-opener' – a stiff canter over about a mile to clean out the windpipe.

That routine may have suited Fred, but there's nothing textbook about it, and the last decade has seen plenty of changes in the ways in which horses are conditioned. Although I used to bombard him with questions about his methods, he always insisted that I'd never do any good if I simply followed what he had done. It was up to me to develop my own way of getting horses fit, as it had been up to him when learning from (but not slavishly following) his father, a noted trainer of an earlier generation.

On our return to the yard at around nine o'clock would come breakfast – a vital part of the day's work for any racehorse trainer. I would usually be wasting to keep my weight down for my next ride and would confine myself to half a slice of toast, Fred and I sitting in the kitchen at a separate table from Di and the girls, talking about entries, ailments and all the thousand other concerns of a racing yard. There was little time for idle chat. Then there were owners to be phoned, entries and declarations to be prepared.

Second lot usually pulled out at nine forty-five and returned at eleven.

I was amazed by just how much responsibility Fred invested in me. He would ask me to go and watch a horse on the gallops and then come back and tell him whether I felt it was fit enough to run or not. How much had the horse blown on the way back to the yard? And pay no attention to what the horse's lad says: he'll say this horse is ready to run, which means that he – the lad – is ready for a day at the races. He always encouraged me to work things out for myself, to stand on my own feet.

If the yard had runners at two meetings, Fred and Mrs Winter would go to one meeting and I to the other, but most days we went to the races together. The arrangement was that he would drive to the races and I would drive back, and those drives themselves formed an important part of the daily ritual. On the way to the races Fred was rarely talkative, and stable jockey John Francome and I had an ongoing game about which of us could be longer in the car with the Guv'nor without Fred speaking: I once managed to get from Lambourn to Windsor without his uttering a single word. On the way back, when I took over the driving, he would usually go to sleep – and I would usually get lost. The knack when this happened, to avoid being caught out, was never, however lost I got, to put the car into reverse in order to manoeuvre myself back towards the right road, as Fred would wake up once he sensed the car going backwards. Once on the way back from Newmarket I got into a complete mess with my sense of direction and ended up the wrong side of Heathrow Airport, only for Fred to wake up as I drove tentatively along the perimeter road.

'What the fuck are we doing here?'

'Sorry, Guv'nor – diversion off the motorway.'

'You've always got an answer, haven't you?'

But I had less of an answer when we were pulled over by the police near Cirencester for speeding on our return from Worcester. Fred was marking up the newspaper with the racing results as they came through on the radio, and didn't even look up as the police signalled to me to stop, came up to the car and listened to my mumbled apologies. The policeman let me off with a warning and we carried on with our journey, though Fred had still made no acknowledgement whatsoever of our little brush with the law. Then after a while he turned to me and said:

'Fulke Walwyn had a double.'

(Surprisingly perhaps, Fred Winter was a demon at playing pool. When things were quiet in the summer we would often go off to have a look at a horse in some remote part of the country, and would stop in a pub for lunch. On one such occasion Fred casually suggested a game of pool, and absolutely thrashed me. He rarely lost.)

We would normally be back in the yard for that other major ritual, evening stables at around five-thirty. This involved going round to each box and giving its occupant a quick once-over. Each horse would have been mucked out and brushed over. As the Guv'nor walked in the lad would stand the horse up and take its rug off, and Fred would run his hands down each of its forelegs – he seldom paid much attention to the hind legs, since horses are far less susceptible to problems in that area – and down its back, all the while asking the lad about each individual horse's condition. I would stand behind the Guv'nor with a notepad and jot down the relevant remarks. Just when the horse thought the examination was over, Fred would slap it in the rib cage: he always liked to see how they tensed their muscles, as that was a good indication of well-being.

I learned so much about horses from simply being near Fred Winter that my debt to him is incalculable. I particularly enjoyed witnessing him at the sales, examining horses with his old friend Eddie Harty. Eddie, who had ridden Highland Wedding to win the Grand National in 1969, was a great judge of a horse, and Fred would often seek his advice when buying. I'd pepper them with questions: what's so good about that one, what's wrong with the other one? Fred and Eddie, well aware that it was simply not done to cavil about a horse's conformation while in the presence of its connections, would wait until we'd left that horse's box before quietly intimating why they had rejected a certain horse. Go back, they'd say, and have a good look at his off foreleg. In that way, padding along behind these two great judges of horseflesh, I absorbed many valuable lessons about what to look for in a horse.

As the end of my first season as assistant trainer approached, Uplands was locked in a close battle with Nicky Henderson for the trainers' championship. Any year it would have meant a huge deal to Fred to win the title, but this duel had the added spice of Nicky's having been assistant trainer at Uplands, and while Fred was delighted to see his protégé doing so well, he was damned if he was going to be beaten by his former deputy. The last few weeks of the season were almost unbearably tense, the more so when our good chaser Plundering won the Whitbread Gold Cup, the last big chase of the spring. In the event the trainers' title was not decided until the very last week of the season, Nicky beating Fred by under £14,000 in prize money, but long before then it had reached the point where I was trying to avoid taking rides for the yard as I didn't want to be the one who screwed up and cost us the title.

The following season Nicky won the title again while Uplands slipped to eleventh place, though the season included a personal high for me: riding Observe to win the Foxhunter Chase at the Cheltenham Festival.

In spring 1987 I heard through Paul Cole, who trained at nearby Whatcombe, that one of Henry Cecil's assistant trainers was leaving and there might be a vacancy. I had been long enough in the jumping game to know that the rewards there are scanty compared with what was on offer on the Flat, and with Henry Cecil maintaining his position as the king of Flat trainers this was a highly tempting prospect – always assuming that I could get the job, which was by no means guaranteed. Paul Cole had already approached Henry on my behalf, so I thought I'd better discuss the position with Fred myself.

Meanwhile Sheikh Ali Abu Khamsin, one of Fred's top owners who had the likes of Fifty Dollars More and Half Free in the yard, had got wind of the idea that I might be looking to move on and asked me to visit him at his home in Devon.

Sheikh Ali told me straight. 'You are a very stupid boy. You will never make any money training National Hunt horses. Come and work for me and I will make you money' – not, as it turned out, by training horses, but by moving to Morocco and running three of the Sheikh's hotels there.

Back in Lambourn it was time to talk all this over with Fred. After evening stables, over a drink in the house, he pointed out that his own retirement could not be too far off – probably just a couple of years – and it would be very inconvenient for him to have to find and then train another assistant at that stage. Give me your word that you won't go off and work for someone else, he said, and I'll give you mine that you can take over from me at Uplands. That way there would be a degree of continuity for the owners and staff (and for the horses), and Fred would still be around to give what support he could. We had a deal.

I don't think Fred ever mentioned this conversation to anyone else. It was a private agreement which would come into effect in the fullness of time. But then, a few weeks later, events intervened.

On Saturday 5 September 1987 we went racing at Stratford with the trainer Charlie Nelson. I'd never seen Fred in such relaxed form. As I had to play in a cricket match in Oxfordshire the following day I left Fred at Stratford and went off to stay at my mother's house – where at about eight o'clock the following morning the phone rang. It was Jo Winter, Fred's daughter: he had taken a bad fall downstairs, and was in hospital. I shot back to Uplands.

It later transpired that Fred had had a stroke, which left him without the power of speech, and it was clear that he would be out of action for a while. So the first task was to phone round all the owners and explain what had happened. Initially the party line was that Fred would get better and return to take over the reins at Uplands again, and for months this was widely expected, both within the yard and outside. The top priority in the immediate aftermath of his accident was damage limitation, and for me that meant making sure we didn't lose any horses from the yard while Fred's owners were waiting for him to get back. Fred was a man who inspired great loyalty in his owners – as indeed he did in his staff – but the circumstances at Uplands at that period were so fraught and uncertain that there was a real danger of horses being removed. In the event not a single one was: another demonstration of what the owners thought of Fred, and of his family.

I've always believed that you cannot train racehorses by committee, and all the most successful yards bear the indelible stamp of the man or woman at the top. The support team can help and advise as well as implement instructions, but you have to have one person in charge. Now we were faced with the situation where that one person was incapacitated and his assistant far too wet behind the ears to be a serious proposition for taking up the reins. Some form of committee – Di Winter and the girls with myself, stable jockey Peter Scudamore and Brian Delaney – was the only solution, and we prayed that it would be a very temporary one.

It was a situation strewn with problems. On the one hand, Uplands was the Winters' business. Most of the owners went back with the family a very long way and were much closer to them than to myself or Brian. On the other hand, Fred had never liked women interfering in any way in the yard. This created a situation where one half of the committee (female) was taking decisions and making plans in the kitchen, while the other half (male) was formulating different plans out in the yard. Jo rode out every day and she and Di naturally had their own ideas about what should be happening with the horses – but equally understandably, when they questioned the horses' breakfast diet, Brian Delaney didn't welcome that sort of input. The matter of where to run can also be pretty subjective, and it is highly unlikely that the same two people will agree about the campaigns of forty horses.

This state of affairs couldn't last very long, and it didn't. Brian and I agreed that it was becoming a classic case of 'too many cooks', and on the basis that we would back each other up, we went to see Di Winter and put it to her: if they wanted us to do the job we would be happy to get on with it, but we had to be left alone to do so. This was not an easy conversation but it cleared the air, and thereafter things settled down.

For me, there were two sides to what was undeniably a very unhappy period of my career.

In the credit column, I had been granted an extraordinary opportunity to make a name for myself at a very young age. The owners were very supportive of me and never offered any criticism of what Brian and I were doing with the horses. Another plus was that in Celtic Shot, who at the time of Fred's accident was one of the most promising young hurdlers in the country, we had a horse who could keep the yard in the headlines.

But there was a debit side which put a much darker complexion on that time. I don't think anyone could begin to understand just how difficult it is to run somebody else's yard for them, and I was keenly aware that although the owners were (in my presence, at least) very supportive, everything I did was being closely scrutinised, leading to the position where everything had to be a compromise. It was impossible for Brian and I not to carry on in the way we thought the Guv'nor would have wanted us to, yet Fred had always insisted that 'you'll never be any good if you just copy me' and he was quite right: we weren't.

Inevitably for what we assumed was a holding operation, decisions were fudged in an attempt to try to make everyone happy. Some of the horses we ran were nothing like fit enough, but we were trying to keep them in one piece: we were worried about being too hard on them, and yet I've never known a successful trainer who wasn't hard on his horses.

The importance of carrying on the day-to-day running of the stable meant that there was little time to consider the wider picture, but when I did so it was becoming increasingly depressing. I was very fond of the Guv'nor (at least, after ten o'clock in the morning) and as it became clear that his injuries were more long-term than we'd first hoped the whole atmosphere around the yard sank to a lower and lower ebb.

For the Winter family, the strain was immense, not least because Fred was the focus of everything: the whole family operated around him, and essentially for him. Fred was more 'king of the castle' than any other man I've ever encountered, and in the aftermath of the accident the family had an extra dilemma to deal with, even though they might not have realised it at the time. If we who had taken up the reins did badly, then the yard would fall to pieces, which apart from the blow to the Winters' considerable pride in their reputation could be disastrous financially, leaving a tottering operation for the Guv'nor to come back to, if and when he could. Our failure would, however, underline how brilliant he had been and how irreplaceable he was. On the other hand, if we did very well the yard would keep going with its reputation intact, but the Guv'nor would look dispensable. With all the turmoil in the family I doubt whether that thought gave them much pause at the time, but it preyed on my mind, and I found the idea very oppressive.

One of the biggest owners in the yard was David Bott, whose horses ran under the name of his company R. E. A. Bott (Wigmore Street) Ltd: at the time of Fred's accident he had such good horses as Observe and Admiral's Cup at Uplands. His reaction to the situation with Fred was an extremely positive one, a real vote of confidence: he asked me to buy him a good horse, giving me a generous budget. I'd heard about a horse in France who sounded as if he might fit the bill. He was due to run in a hurdle race at Auteuil one Sunday shortly after Fred's fall, so Scu and I flew across to Paris to watch him. He absolutely bolted up, and we returned to England determined to acquire him for David Bott – but he, when I told him of his potential new purchase, decided he didn't want a French-bred after all as Fred had never bought him horses in France: go to Ireland, he said, and buy me a horse by one of those good jumping sires Buckskin or The Parson.

It's true that Fred was not accustomed to buying young horses in France, and French-breds were not then nearly as popular among the jumping fraternity as they are now, but none the less I was disappointed by David's rejection of this lovely horse – and more disappointment followed when I failed to find anyone else to buy him.

Scu was beginning to combine his commitment to Uplands with riding for Martin Pipe, and he asked me whether I'd mind if he told Martin about this French horse. I could hardly stand in his way (though I suppose I might have asked for an agent's commission!), and Martin (who to the best of my knowledge had not been attracted to the French market until then) duly bought the horse for around £40,000 – a tidy sum, but it turned out to be a bargain. For this horse was Rolling Ball, who won many good races for Martin including the Sun Alliance Novices' Chase at the Cheltenham Festival in 1991.

Having had to pass up the opportunity of bringing that good horse to Uplands, I duly went to Ireland and from Timmy Hyde's yard bought an unnamed four-year-old by Buckskin: a half-brother to Gaye Brief (who won the Champion Hurdle in 1983), another very good horse, Gaye Chance, and about ten other winners. He was as well-bred an untried horse as you could wish to find, and after a little persuasion Mr Bott agreed to pay a good deal more than what Rolling Ball would have set him back. This horse was the last foal of his distinguished dam Gaye Artiste, and as David Bott was homosexual and insisted that this would be his last racehorse, I suggested we call him The Last Gaye. He told me not to be such a cheeky bugger, and named the horse Black Humour – rather an appropriate name, since the creature, while developing into a very fine racehorse, was responsible for Peter Scudamore breaking his leg in a hurdle race at Market Rasen in November 1990, and has the rare distinction of having fallen in the Grand National, Cheltenham Gold Cup and Champion Hurdle.

Gradually things at Uplands got back to a semblance of normality, though uncertainty about the future continued to make this a very difficult period. So did the perfectly understandable attempts of the Winter family to keep Fred involved, however remotely, with the stable routine. After he had come out of hospital and returned to the house to continue what we assumed would be a finite convalescence, he would be taken round evening stables to look at the horses. He could not, however, utter any coherent words, even an intensive course of speech therapy failing to do much apparent good, and when every night after evening stables I went into the house to tell him about the horses, it was distressing to witness how annoyed he became that he could not make himself understood, could not make me realise which horse he was asking about. Nor could he write things down. Fred simply could not communicate in detail with the outside world.

By the beginning of December 1987, three months after the accident, we were beginning to face the fact that Fred would never train again – and at the same time were beginning to realise just what a wonderful prospect we had in Celtic Shot.

A gelding by Celtic Cone, Celtic Shot had been sent to Fred by his owner and breeder David Horton. There had been easier owners in the yard than David Horton – the number of trainers he had been through bore witness to that – but he did know his horses, as Fred was to discover with Clutterbuck. When David Horton insisted to Fred that Clutterbuck did not thrive on oats, the Guv'nor ignored him. The horse duly lost condition, so Fred bowed to Horton's request and fed him nuts – and Clutterbuck, somewhat to Fred's annoyance, started to thrive. Sadly, however, the horse had to be put down after another horse kicked him during exercise that Christmas Eve and broke his leg; so Celtic Shot's climb up the ladder was a welcome change of fortune for his owner.

Celtic Shot started the season which would lead to the Champion Hurdle with a twenty-length victory in a handicap hurdle at Sandown Park in October 1987, but it was when he won the valuable Allinson Bread Handicap Hurdle at Cheltenham's Mackeson meeting the following month that we were convinced he was heading for the top. In early December he landed another valuable handicap, the Mecca Bookmakers Hurdle at Sandown, and although he carried only 10st 6lb that day, his win was so convincing that we started to think seriously in terms of the Champion Hurdle, a view not in any way dented by victory in the New Year's Day Hurdle at Windsor.

Throughout this period the absolutely crucial factor in my own position was to maintain my working relationship with Brian Delaney. The head lad may not have been thrilled by the arrival of the Old Etonian wannabe stable lad four years earlier, and kept to himself – at least from me – his reaction to the news two years earlier that I was about to become assistant trainer. But after Fred's fall the stable was in crisis, and it was vital that we pulled together. Nothing to that effect was ever expressed between us – it was just understood, and there grew up between us a genuine mutual respect, as indeed there did between myself and Scu, whose input during those difficult months proved a vital element in our pulling through.

In the middle of January, about two months before the Champion Hurdle, Brian came to me and made the suggestion that I plan every single day of the remaining eight weeks of Celtic Shot's preparation. That way we would, he said, cover our arses. And so we plotted every day – every trot, every canter, every gallop. The horse was pretty fit and in very good form, and between the New Year's Day Hurdle and the Champion Hurdle one race would be sufficient to bring him to his peak. Unfortunately that race – the Lee Cooper Hurdle at Sandown Park in February – gave us our only serious wobble. Celtic Shot started odds-on in a field of seven but was beaten eight lengths by the very good hurdler Celtic Chief, trained by Mrs Mercy Rimell. On the face of it this seemed quite a reverse, but Scu reported that there had been a patch of false going crossing the Flat track approaching the straight, just as he was asking Celtic Shot to make up ground. The horse had temporarily floundered there, and the result did not reflect the true form. That was something of a relief, and back at Uplands we resumed Celtic Shot's carefully planned preparation.

The horse's final major piece of work was on Saturday 5 March, ten days before the Champion Hurdle, and we chose his galloping companions carefully: Deep Treasure (ridden by a very promising young jockey named Vivian Kennedy), a top-class young horse who had won his last race at Sandown Park, and Drumlin Hill (ridden by our amateur Charlie Farrell), a five-year-old about whom we were very excited: he had won the Rossington Main Hurdle at Doncaster in January and looked a great prospect. Peter Scudamore came down to ride Celtic Shot, as he always did for the major pieces of work. (Celtic Shot's lad Paul McCormack rode him on other days.) It is always dangerous working good horses together, as it's important that work remains just that and does not turn into a race. For that reason good work riders are highly valuable to a trainer.

Eddie Fisher, the head gallops man in Lambourn and an absolute star, had opened up a fresh piece of ground on 'our strip' for us to work on. This gallop sweeps around the foot of the downs before turning left-handed uphill, and for the first mile all was going well as the three horses worked upsides. I had my eyes fixed on Celtic Shot, then suddenly noticed that Charlie Farrell had started to pull up Drumlin Hill – the horse had fractured a hind leg. Scu shouted at Viv Kennedy on Deep Treasure to keep going, as he knew that Celtic Shot had to finish his piece of work and there was nothing that could be done to help poor Drumlin Hill.

Thank God for mobile phones. The vet came straight away and Drumlin Hill was rapidly put down. This was a terribly bitter blow. He was a lovely big chasing type by champion sire Deep Run out of a mare who had won the Galway Plate, and I really thought he was going to be a star. So did his owner Lady Joseph, who had only had the horse a couple of months but believed in him as much as I did. It struck me as we went back to the yard that morning that even if Celtic Shot won the Champion Hurdle, that would not make up for the loss of Drumlin Hill, and it didn't. That gallop had two more tragic footnotes: within six months Viv Kennedy had been killed as the result of injuries he received in a fall at Huntingdon, and Deep Treasure had died of a heart attack at Ascot.

Celtic Shot arrived at Cheltenham at his peak, and I was convinced that we'd produced him spot-on. Now all we needed was some luck.

There were twenty-one runners in the 1988 Champion Hurdle, and with that size of field plenty of things can go wrong. Celtic Chief started hot favourite at 5–2, with Cloughtaney, trained by Paddy Mullins, second favourite. Celtic Shot, whose chance had seemed to the world outside Uplands (though not inside) to diminish after that Sandown race, started at 7–1, and among the others was an unknown quantity from France named Marly River, who had come over a week before the race and been boarded at Lambourn, where his trainer Yves Porzier got us very confused by subjecting the horse to the equivalent of Celtic Shot's final gallop every day for six consecutive days! Either that man was a genius or he had seriously underestimated the stiffness of the Lambourn gallops, and had it worked out we'd all have had to revise our methods. As it turned out we didn't need to, since Marly River finished well down the field.

About the race itself I can't remember too much except that Scu rode an absolute blinder – a brilliant, positive race. He was bang there at the top of the hill – just as he knew the Guv'nor would have expected – and having taken the lead looked like being collared by the Irish Champion Hurdle winner Classical Charm going to the last, then stayed on up the hill to win by four lengths.

My overwhelming feeling was not of triumph but of

sheer relief. We had not cocked it up. I had trained the winner of the Champion Hurdle – except that I hadn't, of course: the licence was still in Fred's name, and later I was touched to hear Brian Delaney's account of how, having watched the race on television back at Uplands, he had gone over to the Winters' house. Although the Guv'nor couldn't talk, he was completely aware of what had happened and was beaming from ear to ear.

Meanwhile back at Cheltenham I was dying for a fag, and managed to scrounge one from the cigarette case in the Queen Mother's box when I was taken up there for a drink after the race. She's a wonderful lady, and understands that people can get tense over horse races and need the odd ciggie to calm them down.

One of my owners had offered me the services of his daughter as my driver for Cheltenham week, and on the way back to my mother's that evening I took advantage of the luxury of being chauffeured to stop in for a few celebratory drinks with my cousin Ron Brooks and his wife Valerie (daughter of the famous handicapper Geoffrey Freer), and then with my mother's neighbours Mike and Angela Bell. Then it was back to my mother's for a large dinner party. At the end of the evening everyone else – including my rather comely chauffeuse – had gone to bed, and as I reflected on the events of the day over a large glass of whisky I came to the conclusion that by far the best way of celebrating winning the Champion Hurdle would be to go and jump into bed with my driver.

I tiptoed along the corridor so as not to alert my mother to my plans regarding the guest in the room next door to her, and told myself to be positive, taking all my clothes off on the landing and quietly opening the door. To minimise the chances of the object of my affections raising the alarm I shot across the room in the dark and jumped into bed, and after a couple of minutes of quietly waking her up she came to life. I was well along with the major business of the evening when a voice whispered in my ear: 'You do realise you're in the wrong room, don't you?'

Celtic Shot ran once more that season, falling in the Welsh Champion Hurdle. That was a slight setback, but there was always next season to look forward to. What a chaser he'd make!

But the really dark cloud over Uplands was not getting any brighter, and by the end of that season the inevitable could no longer be held off. Fred's progress was very slow. He clearly was not in any position to be held responsible for what went on in the yard, and the Jockey Club understandably took the view that he could not continue to hold the training licence.

It was time for me to become a trainer in my own right.

4

'TRAINED BY C. P. E. BROOKS'

Having gone through the formalities of being granted the licence to train at Uplands, I took over the reins officially at the start of the 1988–9 season.

The presence in the yard from day one of my 'official' training career of a horse as good as Celtic Shot was both a major boost and a disadvantage. On the credit side I'd be training a horse who would be aimed at major races and would keep the yard in the headlines. On the debit side, training Celtic Shot put me instantly in the limelight, and such attention might not necessarily prove welcome as I found my feet and felt my way as a trainer in my own right.

After being a little disappointing earlier in the season, at Cheltenham Celtic Shot turned in a very good performance to finish third in the Champion Hurdle behind

Beech Road and Celtic Chief, beaten three lengths after laying far out of his ground and coming from nowhere in the closing stages. Scu had got a right old kicking when Elementary fell in the first race that afternoon, and at the time I did wonder whether he was a little concussed when he went out to ride Celtic Shot. But in fairness it has to be said that the race was run in a time three seconds slower than the novice hurdle that afternoon, so they probably just went too slowly and left Celtic Shot behind when they quickened up, only for him to stay on at the end. Such an interpretation of the race would certainly fit the theory that he needed a longer distance.

After Cheltenham he had only Dis Train opposing him in the Welsh Champion Hurdle, and having seen him dispose of that opponent at 7–1 on we set our sights on the Aintree Hurdle over two and a half miles on Grand National afternoon. Here he renewed his Cheltenham rivalry with Beech Road, and in view of the increase in distance was well fancied to turn the tables. Celtic Shot started 5–2 favourite, with Beech Road, the reigning champion, only fifth choice in the market at 10–1.

Celtic Shot clearly needed a trip now. Unfortunately David Horton insisted that Scu make plenty of use of him, and having gone ten lengths clear turning into the straight he tied up on the run-in, allowing Beech Road to go past and score an easy win, with Celtic Shot just losing second place to Cloughtaney on the line. It was a classic case of an owner telling a champion jockey how to ride a race and getting it wrong, but to his credit David Horton took full blame for that defeat.

Celtic Shot was our flagship during that first season,

Early days.

(*Left*) With Christopher and Annabel. Our mother didn't believe in wasting money on haircuts.

(*Below*) With mother and father.

(*Bottom*) Not only was I totally incompetent on ponies, I was also extremely nervous.

An Eton education.

(*Left*) We were all very impressed with *Chariots of Fire* ...

(*Below*) Eton has self-elected prefects known collectively as 'Pop'. My suitability as poacher turned gamekeeper material was questionable.

(*Left*) Taking part in the British finals of the tetrathlon at Stoneleigh, Warwickshire.

rly efforts in the saddle.

(*above*) On Deep And Even at Nottingham. Although the horse looks to be going well, he actually fell at this fence and I broke my collarbone. I was never allowed to ride him again. (*Kenneth Bright*)

(*below*) The mad Fionnadoir – man and beast in perfect harmony! (*Michael Haslam*)

Young amateur jockeys in characteristic poses.
(*Above*) On the right is Charlie Egerton; on the left is Richard Dunwoody.
(*Below*) Mark Bradstock at Ascot. (*Paddock Studios*)

...ith the Guv'nor at Kempton Park, January 1987. (*Gerry Cranham*)

...misunderstanding with Hazy Sunset at the last fence at Ascot in April 1987 – but ...uch to the disappointment of Tim Thomson Jones we still won. (*Kenneth Bright*)

The hunter chaser Gratification was an armchair ride.
(*Above*) Being led in by Charlie Farrell after winning at Cheltenham in October 1986 (with my long-suffering mother looking on). (*Bernard Parkin*)
(*Below*) Upsides Peter Scudamore: when Scu saw this photo, he advised me to sit furth back at my fences while we were riding for the same yard.

e highlight of my riding life, winning the Christies Foxhunter Chase on Observe at
eltenham in 1987.

ove) In the snow on the first circuit. (*Kenneth Bright*)

elow) The Guv'nor's post-race debriefing: 'I'll kill you if you forget to weigh in.'
ddock Studios)

Riding Insure (striped sleeves) in the 1987 Grand National.
(*Above*) Crossing Becher's Brook first time round. (*John Crofts*)
(*Below*) Attacking the Chair. (*Kenneth Bright*)

but the distinction of being the first winner credited to C. P. E. Brooks goes to an old gelding called Chalk Pit. David Loder, who was then racing manager to his cousin Roddy Fleming, had arranged for this horse, who had been running in point-to-points, to come to us in the early part of the season while the ground was firm. On his arrival at Uplands, Chalk Pit looked bloody awful – all skin and bones – so I decided to give him a few shots of Nandrolin, a steroid used in those days on horses who were lacking in muscle bulk. In order to avoid failing the post-race dope test it was essential to stop applying the drug at least six weeks before running, but even so in Chalk Pit's case the effect was remarkable: he duly won his first three chases of the season, at Exeter (then called Devon and Exeter), Hereford and Cheltenham, which far exceeded our expectations.

We also did well with some of the Guv'nor's horses, but relations between the new regime at Uplands and the old were not always smooth. The Guv'nor still owned the yard, and his family expected to be kept informed about what was going on, a duty in which I was not always as conscientious as I might have been. At Aintree for the Grand National meeting I received a right dressing-down from Jo Winter for failing to phone Uplands with news of the previous day's runners. Di Winter was quite right to be annoyed. I'd got stuck into a good party in the car park after racing and had forgotten to phone in.

We ended the season with forty-one winners: a respectable total, though not enough to put us anywhere near the top of the trainers' table.

What I have always loved about Lambourn is the way people welcome you into the community. Whatever your age or social background, you're encouraged to join in. No single figure personifies that aspect of the village and its environs better than Peter Walwyn. 'Big Pete', one of the very best trainers in the land and the driving force behind mobilising the different factions in Lambourn for their common good, has the most incredible love and enthusiasm for racing, and has done more for the spirit of community in the area than any single person.

Peter is also particularly remarkable for the extraordinary shape of his training career. In the mid-1970s he was top of the tree, thanks not only to the brilliant Grundy, winner of the Derby in 1975 as well as the 'Race of the Century' against Bustino in that year's King George VI and Queen Elizabeth Diamond Stakes, but also to other top-class horses. So successful was he, in fact, that he became known as 'Pattern Race Pete'. Then things went wrong. He was one of the first Lambourn trainers to be deeply affected by sickness in his horses, and unfortunately for him this happened at a time when reliable tests were not readily available, and so he was dealing with the unknown. His stables fell into the doldrums and he never scaled the same heights again; but he lost none of his enthusiasm for the game. Of all the top trainers over the years, none has put more back into the sport – nor into country life – than Peter Walwyn. I've never met a man quite like Peter, and I'm by no means the first person to see him as the Basil Fawlty of racing: an eccentric, occasionally irascible, often unpredictable but ultimately lovable man.

One of Pete's great passions was staging the annual Lambourn Lurcher Show (which sadly is no more, the event having been given up as the travellers kept cutting people's ears off). PW decided he'd try his luck at the archery display, but as he was doing so it started to bucket down with rain, and the man in charge of archery decided to call it a day, telling Pete: 'I'm packing up, Guv: don't want to get my bows soaked.'

'What?' demanded Pete, working himself up into a fit of which Basil Fawlty himself would have been proud. 'Packing up? Bloody marvellous. Fat lot of good you'd have been at Agincourt.'

The bedraggled archer, unimpressed, started to pack up his gear, bidding a farewell to the great trainer with the parting shot: 'Good job you weren't at Agincourt – otherwise we'd all be speaking French.'

Pete was one of the leading lights in establishing the Open Day at Lambourn, now held annually on Good Friday, when most of the yards in the village open their doors to a vast and highly appreciative throng of visitors.

Less palatable company, at least as far as I was concerned, was another of the great characters of the valley. Over the years the schooling ground in Lambourn has been a pretty lively place to be during first lot. Teaching horses to jump is a tense affair, as mistakes can be costly, and there tend to be plenty of bellowed instructions as trainers harangue their jockeys and lads into getting it right. But nobody was more vocal than Jenny Pitman. How her lads were supposed to concentrate on the job in hand while facing a barrage of advice and verbal abuse from her, God only knows.

It was during one of these sessions that I received my own first dose of the Pitman treatment.

'Oi!' she yelled. 'I want a word with you. You've been going behind my fucking back. Your guv'nor would never have done anything like that.'

She had a point – just. Terry Ramsden, a huge gambler and owner on a large scale, had hit trouble and put all his racehorses on the market. I had made enquiries about some of these – one of which was trained by Mrs Pitman – through Ramsden's racing manager. I could understand why she felt aggrieved that I had not made my approach through her, but I was a keen young trainer not too bothered by such niceties, and I was damned if I was going to be bollocked in public.

'Don't talk to me about ethics,' I countered. 'We had a horse coming back from a hobday operation the other day and your office wouldn't tell me where we could get decent paper bedding from. Fred wouldn't have done that, either.'

The vet had advised us to use paper bedding to reduce the dust in the box while this horse was recovering from the operation on its windpipe, and suggested we consult the Pitman yard since he knew they had a good supplier. They refused, even though they were aware it was for a convalescent animal.

Jenny Pitman was a very fine trainer of staying chasers and had a knack of buying a very nice type of horse. She has also been a colourful character in a sport that needs better promotion, and such characters play a vital part in profile-raising. But did she not get up the noses of some other Lambourn trainers! She practically invented the concept of bullshit single-handedly; and in comparison with this woman, the Labour government's army of spin doctors are a bunch of amateurs.

What really bugged plenty of her fellow trainers was her constantly repeated soundbite: 'I love my horses.' This sentiment was of course a perfectly legitimate marketing ploy, but there was always the implication that she loved her horses more than other trainers did, and looked after them better. In fact she was as hard on her horses as any of the other top trainers have been.

You have to take your hat off to Jenny for the way in which she has manufactured her public image and kept it burnished over the years. For a start, she's a female in what is predominantly a man's world, and as her exposure in the media increased she soon had the newspapers and broadcasters as well as the public eating out of her hand. Her predisposition to tearfulness – her plumbing is more efficient than Thames Water's – hasn't done her any harm, either. The racing media were happy to play along: she was always good copy, and every sports journalist has a sports editor to keep happy.

She was also very quick to pick a fight in any meeting, which in some ways was very useful: she has never been afraid of pointing out things that are wrong. At other times, though, she seemed to pick an argument just for the sake of it.

Several of the elements which make up the Pitman persona came together at the 1998 Grand National. The going at Aintree was very wet indeed, and with two races having been run over the National course earlier in the meeting, the ground was obviously going to be very cut up. But it was so wet and sloppy that the track was going to ride the same as it would have done if it had not been used at all. I had no hesitation in running Suny Bay, and Mrs Pitman ran Nahthen Lad. She then caused a huge amount of fuss after the race by claiming – in a letter to the chairman of Aintree which was somehow leaked to the press – that the ground had been unsafe for the race.

You can't have it both ways. If you love your horses so much, how can you run them on ground you consider unacceptable? Would Jenny's adoring public, who responded to her caring image so enthusiastically, have expected her to subject her horses to intolerable conditions?

Racing will miss Mrs Pitman, but those gallops have fallen eerily silent since she has removed herself from the scene.

Another great character – and one loved among the training fraternity – was Captain Tim Forster, who sadly died early in 1999.

The Captain, last of the old school to train expertly both his horses and the people who owned them, was noted for his pessimism, which was probably a defence against the awful surprises and disappointments which lurk around the corner for anyone involved in racehorses. That pessimism was most famously expressed when before the 1980 Grand National he legged up American amateur rider Charlie Fenwick on to Ben Nevis with the words: 'Keep remounting.' As so often, the pessimism was misplaced: Ben Nevis won.

Having trained for many years at Letcombe Bassett, not far from Lambourn, towards the end of his career the Captain moved to a new yard at Downton Hall in

Shropshire: he had been ill for some time with multiple sclerosis and probably wanted to spend more time with his friends the Wiggins, who owned Downton Hall and loved doing the things the Captain loved.

Miriam and I were his first guests in Shropshire, staying with him for the christening of my godchild Tara Wiggin. As we were standing in the churchyard after the service, the Captain turned to us and said: 'If you two think you're going to ruin my good name in this county by sleeping together you've got another think coming. I've given you separate rooms – but the doors haven't arrived for any of the rooms in the house yet.'

We had a cracking evening, the highlight of which was a session of 'Squeak, piggy, squeak' with the Captain as 'it'. This meant he had to crawl around in the dark on the floor of the dining room – which was about the size of a tennis court – and when he caught hold of anyone had to squeeze them and shout, 'Squeak, piggy, squeak!' If he could tell who the person was, he or she then had to crawl around the floor with him, holding on to his foot, in search of the next victim. It's difficult to exaggerate how much he enjoyed this.

Eventually the Captain retired for the night, and Miriam did likewise – followed about three hours later by me. It may not come as a total surprise to learn that I was considerably the worse for wear by then – so much so that I had to negotiate the stairs on my knees – but being a romantic sort of bloke I thought I should pop into Miriam's room and give her a goodnight kiss. I crawled through the doorless entrance to her room, and as I pulled myself up on to the bed thought, 'She's snoring a bit tonight!' – then got more of a fright when I pulled the sheet back to kiss her. Thank God the Captain didn't wake up: he'd have got a bit of a fright too.

I shouldn't have been at Downton Hall that weekend at all. I'd told Mark and Philippa Wiggin that I'd be a useless godfather, and they assured me that while they were well aware of that, they still felt their little daughter would benefit from my spiritual guidance. A year and a half later I found myself sitting next to Philippa at the Newmarket house of Sheikh Mohammed's racing manager Anthony Stroud. It had been a long day and I'd had a few in the pub with Fritz.

'How's everything, then, Philippa?'

'Fine,' she replied.

Bit of a pause, then I broke the silence: 'I see the diet's not going too well.'

'Piss off, Charlie: I'm pregnant.'

Now one thing I've learned over the years is that when a girl tells you she's pregnant it's best to sound interested.

'Congratulations! Is it your first?'

Philippa went bonkers.

T he Winters could not sustain the running of Uplands indefinitely, and during the 1988–9 season the yard was put on the market. By the later 1980s the purchase of a racing stable was not the most magnetic of investments, and despite its historic associations Uplands was attracting little interest. Indeed, it wouldn't have surprised me if the only potential buyer had been myself. There was a large measure of sense in my acquiring the yard – if I could finance such a massive undertaking – since that would avoid the huge disruption, for horses and humans alike, of finding somewhere else and moving in.

With hindsight it was a huge mistake for me to try to buy Uplands – I was buying at the height of the market and would end up selling at the bottom – but I was determined to have a go in order to keep horses, owners and staff together. It's easy to see now that what I should have done is rent a smaller yard that I could afford and gone on from there – easy but pointless.

Two factors led me into my great mistake.

The first was Lady Joseph. Eileen was the widow of the tycoon Sir Maxwell Joseph and one of the Guv'nor's most loyal owners; when I first met her she had only just ventured into horse racing through her friend Coral Samuel, owner of Brown Chamberlin. Eileen Joseph had become like a third grandmother to me, as well as a great friend, and to demonstrate her place in my racing life I can't do better than reprint the tribute I wrote for the *Sporting Life*, which was printed under the headline 'Inspirational Lady' following her death in November 1994:

On Wednesday this week, Lady Eileen Joseph died, aged 71, at her new home in Stanford-in-the-Vale. She died suddenly after a fairly short illness, the sort of end she would have wished.

She was never a malingerer. She used to say: 'I don't like being ill, it doesn't suit me.'

Fred Winter bought Eileen her first horse, Gold Bearer, which became her first runner at Newbury in January 1985, beaten a short head under Ben de

Haan, unfortunately by me on Mr Winter's other runner, Deep And Even.

Her last runner, Padre Mio, was also beaten a short head on Tuesday. However, she didn't mind about things like that for herself, only for us.

Newbury was also the first time I met Eileen. She bought me a bottle of champagne after the race because she thought I looked a bit green and could see FTW was none too pleased with the result. It was the beginning of a very rewarding friendship.

She made it her business to support Uplands when FTW retired and totally opened our horizons.

Armed with some knowledge of jumping in France (and Vilma, her sensational cook), she insisted we look for horses in France, which no one else was doing at the time.

All Jeff was her first purchase at Maisons-Laffitte from Alain Chelet, who was later to stable Bokaro for us when he won twice at Clairefontaine and also at Auteuil.

It was on that occasion, when she was ankle-deep in the sand schooling ground at 6.30 a.m., that I had to remind her that I had promised to tell her if she ever became 'a complaining old woman', as she put it.

All Jeff went on to win a chase at Cagnes-sur-Mer, near her home in France, break the track record at Sandown, win at Fairyhouse and fall in the Sun Alliance when bang in contention.

That year, she tried to persuade me to fly All Jeff to Cagnes in case the lorry drivers ate him on the way there.

Bokaro was her favourite horse because he is warm and enthusiastic. He won the Queen Mother Supreme Hurdle at Belmont, the Corsa Siepi di Milano (which the Italian air traffic controllers caused his owner to miss – probably our highest point) as well as his unique win at Auteuil.

We looked for suitable horses in Poland when the French market took off, but Vincent Thieffry, our agent in France, and myself found nothing suitable and brought her home caviar and a Russian tank driver's night-vision set instead.

Without her inspiration, we would have missed so much. She pretended she knew nothing of racing and horses but she knew more than those who think they do. She left everything to her trainer, apart from the odd request . . .

When the recession was biting, a friend of hers announced that she was selling her horses because of the cost, in spite of the fact that she could well afford it. Eileen's reaction was to buy another so that no lad lost a job.

She did more for the staff at Uplands than could be believed. If she had a party – and believe you me, she had the best parties – the lads had just as good a one the next day.

I can remember her asking: 'Do you think the lads would mind if I gave them champagne? It would make things easier with the glasses.' . . .

Generally in life, the less important a person was, the more of a fuss she made of them. I would like to think she enjoyed the short time she lived at Uplands; she loved entertaining.

I can hear her saying: 'Do you think we had better invite Charlie Egerton to lunch? I don't think he gets fed properly!'

She was a real breath of fresh air at Uplands. We loved her for her care and down-to-earth charm.

She will curse us for the selfish tears and nonsense that we have shed in the last few days, but, unfortunately, we know how much we are going to miss her and the fun that we all had together.

We, in turn, will be sad that none of us had the chance to say goodbye.

More than anything, Eileen loved challenge and innovation, and it was in a pioneering spirit that she and I made our first inroads into France. At that time it was not the fashion to buy French-breds to race over jumps, though the legendary trainer Peter Cazalet had done so well before my time, and her initiative paid off – not least when we followed her insistence that the horses should not only be bought in France, but as often as possible raced there too.

She loved having fun. When Bokaro was due to run in New York she persuaded me that I should be initiated into the delights of Concorde, but since tickets were a bit cheaper if you flew from Paris, we nipped over there and had a stopover at the Grand Hotel. This was her favourite Parisian billet, and every time I visited it with her, she and I would sit up drinking the night away with the manager Frank.

It was on one of these visits to Paris that Lady Joseph decided it was time for me to sample opera – but, thank God, after ten minutes a load of dry ice was belched on to the stage and gave her a coughing fit, so we had an excuse to leave.

Her villa in the South of France provided a welcome retreat when I was trying to escape the gossip columnists during the early stages of my relationship with Miriam Francome, and her cook there, the famous Vilma, is simply the best in the world. Vilma's speciality was foie gras cooked in a hollowed-out brioche soaked in white port, and on a slightly humbler level she showed me how to cook a mean cheese soufflé: the trick is to add beer to the roux, since the bubbles in it help the soufflé to rise.

Another useful hint I got from my association with Lady Joseph was to drink red wine from a magnum, not a bottle: only one cork spoiling the wine rather than two, she said.

She loved hotels and restaurants, and introduced me to some of the finest places in Europe. One I particularly took to was the Colombe d'Or in Saint Paul de Vence – I liked the thought that the Picassos on the walls were real, and had been drawn at the very table at which I was sitting – and it was here that I went with Bruce Urquhart and Philippa Kindersley after Lady Joseph's horse All Jeff had run at Cagnes-sur-Mer. I thought I should buy Bruce a good lunch to thank him for the way he had looked after 'Jeffrey' (who was more like a human being than a horse – maybe I should have taken him as well). Philippa drinks only champagne and takes a bit of laying up with, so I pointed out that I could only afford lunch if she didn't drink at all – otherwise it would have to be lunch in the bar over the road with the *boules* players – and to my amazement she agreed. We ended up sitting at a table next to Ringo Starr, who seemed to have perfected the art of smoking and swallowing his food at the same time, and his presence had attracted a crowd of gawpers at the window. Philippa had not noticed Ringo, and asked what all those people were gawping at. Quick as a flash, Bruce pronounced that the locals had heard that she wasn't drinking and had come to see for themselves . . .

After I had discussed with Eileen my dilemma about the purchase of Uplands and how I was to finance it, she made me a proposition: she would come in with me on a fifty-fifty basis. She would live in the house, and I would train from the yard. This seemed, at the time, an ideal solution, since I had no desire to live in a place as large and grand as the house at Uplands.

A price was agreed, contracts were drawn up, and as far as I was concerned everything was going ahead. Then, just as I thought we were about to complete the purchase, my solicitor received a call from her solicitor to say that the deal was off. Lady Joseph had backed out.

As well as being highly agitated by this news, I was baffled. She and I had agreed everything, so what had happened? There was only one person who could tell me the truth, and try as I might to make contact with her, she had gone to ground – I couldn't get hold of her for love nor money.

When eventually she did emerge and I was able to ask for an explanation, she would only say that her family had talked her out of the deal. I was well aware that her family did not approve of me and took a dim view of my friendship with her, so could only conclude that they had put the mockers on the deal simply because the association was not to their liking.

This left me in a severe quandary. The sale of Uplands had been agreed, and there was now a gaping hole where half the cost – around £600,000 – had been. I had two alternatives: pull out or find the rest of the money myself. Like a prat I did the latter: I went to the bank and borrowed the £600,000. The repayments may have been crippling, but at least I was getting Uplands.

The other factor was the state of the property market. For a while prices had been going up and up, and to a person as naïve as myself there seemed no reason why they should not continue to do so. A collapse in property prices or a recession were phenomena I had never encountered or envisaged. As far as I was concerned, Uplands was expensive, but it was none the less a perfectly good investment.

I took the plunge.

When the 1989–90 season began it was in effect my third season in charge at Uplands, but in many ways it felt like my first. Now that I owned the yard as well as holding the licence, I could do whatever I wanted. Right or wrong, it would be down to me and me alone. I was at last my own master, to stand or fall by my own judgement and my own decisions.

One of the first innovations I tried concerned a good horse we had called Hazy Sunset. In those days, before the programme of summer jumping was introduced, one season ended at the beginning of June and the next began late in July, and with the exception of a few early-season trainers, very few National Hunt yards kept horses in training over the summer. In Hazy Sunset we thought we had a horse who could clean up in some of the early races, so we kept him going through the summer and were rewarded with victories in four races – two at Newton Abbot and the other two at Market Rasen – between the end of July and the middle of October. He also won at Wolverhampton on Boxing Day.

Thanks to Hazy Sunset and others, the season began very well. It was a dry autumn, which meant that good, safe jumping ground was at a premium, and in those days it was still believed that it was worth running a horse half fit first time out since it would inevitably need its first run of the season. Deliberately running a horse half fit is now thought more likely to do harm than good and the practice is now virtually extinct, but we were keen to get races on decent ground into as many of our horses as we could, so I took six of them all the way up to Ayr, the theory being that on their next outings down south they would win, as they'd already had a run. Arden won his Ayr race, and he and Bajan Sunshine duly won next time out.

In November, Arden won the Kennel Gate Novices' Hurdle at Ascot to give Peter Scudamore the 1,139th winner of his career, thus breaking John Francome's record and becoming the winning-most jump jockey in racing history. This was a great landmark – though I often used to joke with Scu that he'd have broken the record the day before on our horse Espy if he'd sat still at the last instead of wrestling the horse to the ground – and I was thrilled that he reached it on one of mine and not on a horse trained by Martin Pipe. (Arden's owner Lord Howard de Walden had not been at Ascot for the race and at first could not understand all the fuss over his horse winning a novice hurdle!)

Everything was going well. When Baies won the Tommy Whittle Chase at Haydock Park in December by a short head from 1987 Cheltenham Gold Cup winner The Thinker, we had had twenty-four winners from fifty-six runners, a pretty decent strike rate by any standards, but exactly what should be happening if you have good horses and they are fit and healthy.

By now Celtic Shot's attention had been switched from hurdles to fences, and despite his occasional jumping lapse over the smaller obstacles, he seemed to take well to chasing. His first outing in a steeplechase was hugely promising – beaten a neck at Chepstow by Waterloo Boy (who had won the previous season's Arkle Chase) – and the day after Baies won at Haydock the same track saw Celtic Shot's first victory over fences. I always liked taking novice chasers to Haydock, as you tend to get small fields there and those big black fences encourage the horses to concentrate on what they are doing. I'm not sure, however, that the jockeys enjoyed my application of this theory quite so much.

On Boxing Day 1989 we had our first overseas winner, All Jeff at Cagnes-sur-Mer. Guy Landau, who had ridden for Stan Mellor before relocating to France, rode him for us. Two weeks later Scu flew down to Cagnes to ride All Jeff in his next race. His plane arrived late and we didn't have time for a proper walk around the course – French jumping tracks tend to be very complicated figures-of-eight and I was terrified that he was going to get lost on the way round – so I made him run round with me, possibly not the ideal preparation for a jockey about to ride in a race. In the end it was all to no avail, as the horse was brought down at the second. Guy Landau was back on board All Jeff for the Grand Prix de la Ville de Nice at the end of January, and we picked up a handy £11,790 for finishing second.

As a young trainer so early in my career I should have been very happy when that season ended. We'd had fifty-six winners at home plus two abroad, and our home prize money totalled over £211,000, less than a third of that netted by champion trainer Martin Pipe but enough to put me ninth in the table. And there had been plenty of highlights in addition to Celtic Shot's establishing himself as a top novice chaser and giving us such hopes for the future. There was a treble at Sandown and a big double at Ascot (Battalion and Okeetee); All Jeff broke the track record for two and a half miles at Sandown Park and won the valuable Tattersalls Novice Chase at Fairyhouse in Ireland; and With Gods Help beat the track record for two miles at Ascot.

But there had been setbacks as well. Abbots View, a promising novice hurdler, had been killed in a fall at Cheltenham on the same day that All Jeff won at Fairyhouse, and the very next day at the same course Arden had injured his knee so badly, skidding into a huge ditch on the perimeter of the track after unseating his rider, that his racing career was over. (One rather over-optimistic Irish breeder read about the accident and phoned to offer Arden a place at his stud – an unusual offer for a gelding to receive.) For me, these were young horses who could not be replaced, and I took such reverses very badly.

I was wrong to do so, of course, and this seemed to me to expose a flaw in my mental approach and indeed to cast doubt on my suitability long-term as a trainer of racehorses. Men of the calibre of Fred Winter or, from another sphere, Alex Ferguson, wouldn't have been thinking so negatively after such a good start. They would have been focusing on the positive, and redoubling their determination to drive on into the future.

The demons of doubt were partly put to flight by a good start to the next season. There were plenty of horses in the yard, they all seemed in good shape, and we had a potential new star in the shape of Bokaro.

I had bought Bokaro for Lady Joseph in France, and since he no longer qualified for novice races and lacked a bit of size we decided to map out an ambitious foreign campaign for him rather than concentrate on the home front. His first target was the Queen Mother Supreme Hurdle at Belmont Park, New York, in October 1990, and although he had run in France in June I felt he needed another race to put him right for America. (I can't now believe that I was thinking in such a backward way.) In the early season there was a lowly race at Perth in which, despite carrying top weight, he was very well treated, and since the ground was safe enough there we decided that was just what was required. In the event Scu got him home only by a length, and in retrospect it had been a bloody stupid thing for me to do. The French hurdles he was used to were very similar to the obstacles he'd be encountering in New York, so why on earth did I want to confuse the poor horse by running him over English hurdles?

John Durkan was dispatched to New York with Bokaro a couple of days before the race, and I flew out on Concorde with Lady Joseph. It was a shame the flight was so short: we'd only just got stuck into the champagne when it was time to prepare for the landing. Still, we managed to startle one air hostess, who was overheard expressing her surprise at the amount that young man and his grandmother had managed to knock back . . .

The Queen Mother Hurdle was a demolition job, with Bokaro never off the bridle. JD and I watched the race in the betting hall at Belmont Park, and rather frightened the natives with our celebrations. That evening we had to go to the post-race ball with Lady Joseph, but we soon managed to get her tucked up in bed, after which we went off on a real bender: JD seemed to know most of the bartenders in New York – a benefit, no doubt, of his being Irish – and we had the night of our lives.

Bokaro's win at Belmont Park was just the beginning of a purple patch. A week later Scu and Espy broke the track record for two and a half miles at Newbury, and we landed a big payday at Wetherby when Celtic Shot won the Charlie Hall Chase and Battalion the West Yorkshire Hurdle.

Little did I know it, but at just twenty-seven years old I was at the peak of my training career. From then on, while getting to the top remained the only thing that would keep me in the game, it was to be downhill all the way.

What happened is simply that our horses started to get sick. We analysed everything and tried anything to get them right, but viral infections and post-viral problems constantly hampered our operation every season from the end of November right through to the spring. Try as we might, we could never get enough horses in the yard healthy enough to maintain our good record.

Our head lad Brian Delaney must have been driven up the wall by the number of times we tried to change the horses' feed, and perhaps I should have left well alone in that department.

To compound the problems of the viral infection in 1990, that November Black Humour managed to break Scu's leg at Market Rasen. This seemed to offer another golden opportunity for Ben de Haan, the stable's second-string jockey, to make his mark, but timing is everything in life and poor Ben reached the hot seat just as the horses were starting to sicken – exactly as had happened when John Francome had retired in 1985. Ben was a great servant to the yard, an exceptionally fine schooling jockey and a good race-rider, though – with the obvious exception of his Grand National win on Jenny Pitman's Corbiere in 1983 – he never seemed to get his fair share of luck.

A number of owners started to suggest that I needed to look for a new stable jockey. Scu, when fit, was riding more and more for Martin Pipe, and in the light of the horses' infirmities and the odd high-profile mishap such as Bokaro at Ascot, I had to tell Ben that he was no longer the automatic pick when Scu was not available. I was very upset at having to do so as Ben had done such a great job for the yard for so long, but I had little choice: the trainer comes under pressure from the owners, and if he doesn't want to lose owners he has to act.

We went into the Cheltenham Festival in March 1991 with high hopes. Celtic Shot had won four big chases that season, most recently a good Gold Cup trial in the Charterhouse Mercantile Chase at Cheltenham in January, and was favourite for the Gold Cup. Espy had won the Fairlawne Chase at Windsor and Black Humour had booked his ticket for the Champion Hurdle with a very impressive win at Kempton. With seven runners, many with major chances, we looked to have a very strong team for Cheltenham. But it all turned to disaster.

The plan for the Champion Hurdle was for Black Humour to be handy, but Jamie Osborne missed the break, which scuppered that idea. He jumped the first flight in last place, and at the second was hit by a swinging hurdle and fell. We should have fitted blinkers on Celtic Shot in the Gold Cup, didn't, and paid the price for our timidity. After running in small fields he didn't seem to enjoy the hurly-burly competitiveness of the Gold Cup. Rather than keep him to the outer as we'd planned, Scu took him down the inner, and the horse didn't like it one bit. He sulked his way into seventh place, way behind the winner Garrison Savannah. Of the others, Gold Cap fell coming down the hill for the last time in the four-miler when in a winning position, and the rest ran badly or just weren't good enough.

If things weren't going too well at home, there was always abroad, and after Bokaro had finished third in the Welsh Champion Hurdle at Chepstow early in April we decided to aim him at the very valuable Corsa Siepi di Milano at San Siro, the Italian equivalent of the Champion Hurdle, later that month. We were sure that Bokaro would be good enough to lift this race so long as we were reasonably discreet about it: taking on Italian hurdlers was one thing, but taking on the best of the English or Irish quite another. Luckily at this stage not too many British trainers were scouring the Milan programme book.

Graham Bradley rode his first winner for me on Switch at Plumpton on 12 April, and the following day flew out to partner Bokaro in Milan, where a win in the Corsa Siepi proved an excellent way of cementing our new relationship. (It is worth noting in passing that Bokaro's wins in the USA and Italy netted about the same as he would have got by winning the Champion Hurdle.)

The consequences of Bokaro running in Milan were rather more far-reaching than winning the Corsa Siepi di Milano.

Miriam Strigner, daughter of a Harley Street psychiatrist, had come to live in Lambourn courtesy of her mother Connie, who at a party in London had met the trainer Ken 'Window' Payne. Ken was moaning about the departure of his secretary, and Miriam's mother saw the ideal opportunity for her little girl back home in Devon, with the result that Miriam arrived in Lambourn to take over the job.

Her first day should have given her due warning about the sort of community she had come into. 'Window' had gone up into the hayloft to fetch a pair of blinkers for his runner that afternoon, having already changed for the races into a thin green summer suit and his best leather shoes. Miriam was working away in the office when the door was flung open and 'Window' staggered in, the colour of his face matching the colour of his suit.

'Miriam, I need your help. I've had a bit of an accident.'

Coming down from the hayloft, he'd slipped on the wooden steps and descended on his arse. The steps were sporting long splinters, and somehow he'd managed to use his wedding tackle as a handbrake.

His green trousers slid down to his ankles as he displayed the damage to Miriam – who, although she had two older brothers, was in no way familiar with what lay before her eyes.

This was no time for first aid, and her reaction – 'Ken, I think I'd better take you down to the doctor's' – was, in the circumstances, probably the right one.

When Ken Payne left Lambourn for Yorkshire, Miriam stayed on to work for Patrick Haslam, and in June 1976 she married John Francome.

After nearly fifteen years of marriage, John and Miriam split up in the spring of 1991. I was very good friends with both of them, having had a horse in John's yard, and regularly played tennis with him. After the split I saw a fair bit of Miriam, though I didn't ask her why she and John parted company (after eight years with her, I still haven't). At that stage we were – genuinely – just good friends, but, understandably, John did not see it quite the same way.

On the weekend Bokaro was running in Milan, Miriam happened to be going to Pisa to see her best friend Candy Sasse and Candy's husband Duncan, who was then training out there, and I suggested that she stop off in Milan on the way. (I don't think Lady Joseph would have minded, but in the event she wasn't there, courtesy of the Italian air traffic controllers.) One thing then led to another, and our relationship changed footing.

Early the next morning the phone in my hotel room rang. It was John. 'Morning, Charlie! Well done on winning that race yesterday.'

Still half asleep, I was mumbling my thanks when he carried on: 'Look, Charlie. One of the newspapers has just told me it's got a photo of you and Miriam in Milan last night. I'd better speak to her to sort out our story so they don't print it next week.'

I still go cold when I think of what I did next. Instead of behaving how any awake individual with half a brain would have done and denying that I had any idea what he was on about, I said 'OK' and handed the phone across to Miriam . . .

The weeks that followed were understandably fraught. I think John burned most of Miriam's clothes, but I can't confirm the story put about in the press that he drove into the yard at Uplands and dumped them on the ground. If that happened, I wasn't there at the time. He did come and remove her car from Uplands, leaving the contents strewn across the drive, and dropped off her chickens in bin liners at Charleston's Place, the house in which I was then living in Eastbury.

John was very angry, and his anger was rooted in the sense of betrayal he felt towards me. I had let him down, and he had every right to feel embittered. I had been a very good friend of his, and yet I had allowed myself to become involved with Miriam with rather unseemly haste after their separation. This was clearly not the way for a friend to behave, and while there is no defence for it there is a reason: I didn't want to be slower off the mark than some of his other friends who may have had a similar move in mind.

Living in such close proximity made life very difficult for everyone. (I think trainer Paul Cole found it most inconvenient, as the rift completely knackered his tennis four.) By and large people in Lambourn tended not to take sides and treated us all very even-handedly, though there was a local lady who did adopt a rather pious stance: interestingly, she had bolted from her husband within a couple of years.

(Predictably enough, my liaison with Miriam proved good cannon fodder for the gossip columnists, but I was not wholly unknown to them. For a while I walked out with Anna Wallace, who as a former girlfriend of the Prince of Wales was a source of constant fascination for the tabloids, and her relationship with a young Hooray Henry racehorse trainer was right up their street. Anna was quite wild, and to have her as Queen of England would have livened things up a fair bit. Her nickname was 'Whipper', but I never found out why. Contrary to popular conjecture, the name supposedly had its origin in the hunting field rather than anywhere else.)

I am pleased to say that John and Miriam get along very well nowadays, and that John and I are again speaking to each other. We don't talk, but we do speak. In another eight years perhaps we'll be playing tennis together again – and by then he'll be beating me, as he's ageing much better than I am.

The 1990–1 season had one more excitement in store. Through my French agent Vincent Thieffry (who had brought Rolling Ball, All Jeff and Bokaro to my attention) I'd bought for about £20,000 a horse named Castigliero, and put together a partnership including Betsy Meade in the USA and Jim McCarthy in London to take him on. Having made the arrangements, I disappeared into hospital to have my tonsils removed by Richard Lavelle, one of Toby Balding's owners: I'd been hoping to chat up Richard after the operation and persuade him to buy a part of Castigliero, but there was no chance, the way I was feeling on coming round.

Vincent Thieffry kindly drove the horse from Chantilly to Lambourn so that he could run in my name, then promptly drove him back to France for his race a couple of days later at Enghien, near Paris. (I should have been ashamed to put a horse through that just so that he could run in my name.) The night before the race I hauled myself from my hospital bed on to a Paris plane for a decent night out with the others, and we duly presented ourselves at Enghien the next day, when the effect of the previous evening's alcoholic anaesthetic was beginning to wear off, though the hospital's version was making me feel very groggy.

Vincent met Jim McCarthy, Betsy Meade and me in the paddock, where we discovered that he'd booked a French jockey who didn't speak any of our native languages – English, Irish or American. Vincent gave the jockey his instructions, and assured us that although there were some twenty runners we only had one to beat. Yet we were 30–1 on the pari-mutuel. Someone was badly wrong. I was just hoping that it wasn't Vincent.

The race was round two circuits. After one circuit Castigliero was last. I was gripping an iron rail in the stand so tightly that blood was beginning to drip on to the floor, and I was longing to be back in that hospital bed. Then slowly but surely Castigliero started making progress – just a little, then a little more – and I began to think that this might have been a respectable purchase after all. He kept making ground, jumped the last in fifth place and then staged a late surge to win by half a length. Within ten days of his purchase the horse bought for

£20,000 had recouped £10,000 in prize money. Vincent had done it yet again.

Whatever money the owners won betting on the horse never left Paris – indeed, never left the racecourse. Six of us started by drinking sixteen bottles of champagne in the cellar of the racecourse – a fairly unusual experience in itself. How I didn't die I'll never know; but I survived both that round of celebration and my tonsil removal to start the new campaign at Uplands that summer.

By now I was financially in big trouble.

Interest rates had gone through the roof, which was making the bank loan I'd taken out to buy Uplands a millstone round my neck. The recession had hit many of my owners badly – who needs a racehorse when the economy collapses? – and the yard had gone from overflowing to only three-quarters full. It was a financial situation which was to cost me my independence and my sanity.

On top of all those worries, the season itself was not a great success. As usual, things started well enough: but then, it always seemed the case that we had little problem with the health of the horses until they started to get sick about November.

Celtic Shot, who was again to be aimed at the Gold Cup, won the Charlie Hall Chase but was just touched off by Auntie Dot in the Edward Hanmer Chase at Haydock Park. He then ran a dismal race to finish last behind Carvill's Hill in the Rehearsal Chase at Chepstow – afterwards he showed signs of having burst a blood vessel, a sure sign that he was ill – and plans to give him a spring campaign were ruined when he developed leg trouble and was retired for the season.

In effect, that was the end of Celtic Shot. Although he tried a comeback he never remotely approached his best. He had done more for us than we could ever do for him, and in a way training him frightened me: I was always thinking, 'I'll never get a horse as good as this one, and what will happen to me after he's gone?'

The season did not turn out a complete disaster, but a total of twenty-nine winners was well short of what I considered satisfactory: I knew that I could still train top horses to win top races, but that wasn't enough, and I found myself getting more and more depressed about the situation.

It wasn't all gloom, though. My Young Man was growing into a very fine chaser, and his six victories won him the Channel Four Trophy for the winning-most horse of the season: such was his progress that he was officially considered to have improved twenty pounds through the season. He won five off the reel before running fourth behind Waterloo Boy, Uncle Ernie and Master Rajh in the Game Spirit Chase at Newbury (where the ground was too quick for him), then proved his toughness by running twice at the Cheltenham Festival. On the opening day he carried top weight in the Grand Annual Chase over two miles, and under an inspired front-running ride from Brad scorched home by twelve lengths. Two days later he was again in action in the Cathcart over two and a half miles: he started favourite but was headed before the last fence and finished third behind Repeat The Dose.

Then there was Parson's Thorns. I'd bought him on spec and persuaded Susan and Gerard Nock – who had a few horses at their place near Stow-on-the-Wold and who were later to hit the headlines with Senor El Betrutti – to take him on, and as he was from the family of one of the Guv'nor's good old horses Paddy's Road House, we harboured great hopes for him. After he'd won a novice chase at Chepstow in January 1992 we took him to Haydock to run on the same day as My Young Man, and I remember thinking on the drive up there: if both these win, will it make any real difference to the mess I've got to sort out? They did, and it didn't.

Both those horses were among our Cheltenham Festival hopes, but like all the others in the yard they seemed wrong. Our vets told us to forget about Cheltenham and give the horses antibiotics, but instead I enlisted the help of Chris Day, a homoeopathic vet. He administered drops and we decided to let the horses take their chance. Parson's Thorns was a 25–1 shot in the Sun Alliance Chase but we thought he had possibilities (despite the opposition including the likes of Miinnehoma, Bradbury Star, Rough Quest and Captain Dibble). He was making progress through the field climbing the hill second time round when suddenly Brad pulled him up. Parson's Thorns had shattered a hind leg and had to be put down. (To make matters worse, if that were possible, I hadn't been able to get an owner to let me buy Parson's Thorns' full brother the year before, so he went to John Edwards instead. The horse was named Monsieur Le Cure, and turned out to be a top-class performer before he, like his brother, was killed in action at Cheltenham.)

Losing horses is very upsetting for all involved, and there were several occasions during my training career when I found myself thinking: 'Should we be doing this?' I console myself with the notion that, by and large, most horses enjoy racing. Those who don't enjoy it usually make that fairly clear through racecourse performance, and eventually will end up doing something else. But whatever view one may have about the level of job satisfaction in horses, losing a good one is always worse for the trainer than losing a bad one. That, of course, does not apply to the horse's lad or lass, and whatever the value of the animal to owner and trainer, it's the stable staff for whom the loss is most upsetting. The lad looks after that horse day in, day out, and knows all its characteristics and foibles. If a lad looks after three horses and one is killed, that is a third of their life destroyed – and not just their working life: most lads get very attached to their horses, so that it is scarcely an exaggeration to say that losing one is akin to losing a member of the family.

Graham Bradley's last ride in April 1999 before being suspended pending his court appearance was at Cheltenham on Country Star, a horse kindly given to my mother by Prince Fahd Salman. Although it might have been too much to expect Brad to sign off with a winner, Country Star had been beaten only about four lengths when fourth in the Grand Annual at the Cheltenham Festival, and was giving Ed James, formerly my assistant, a great chance to show his quality as a young trainer and advertise the skills on which he is building his career. Coming to the third last fence, Country Star was in the lead and going strongly – when all of a sudden Brad pulled him up. The horse had broken a leg, and the end was inevitable.

I felt devastated. Country Star had given everyone (particularly myself) such a thrill with his run at the

Festival, and now he was just a carcass. My mother and her co-owner Stella Towler knew whom this incident affected most, and thought only of Ed James and of the horse's lass Sarah: driving back to East Garston with the empty horsebox was desperately demoralising. It's the empty box back at the yard that evening which hurts deepest. (I heard that a couple of weeks later Brad, with characteristic kindness, had bought Sarah dinner.)

Nor is it much fun riding a horse that gets killed. The first time it happened to me was on a horse of Oliver Carter's called Athford. Oliver trained lots of good horses – he won the Whitbread Gold Cup with Otter Way in 1976 – and thought nothing of pitching his horses in with the very best. I was riding Athford in the Horse and Hound Cup at Stratford when he did the splits after landing over the third last and broke his back. Walking back across the course and handing the bridle to a poor lass in tears was a nightmare.

The second time was when I was riding Compton Lad for Bobby McAlpine and Bridget Broad at Ascot in April 1985. I'd finished fourth on him at the Cheltenham Festival and at that stage he was far and away the best horse I'd ridden – a real gentle giant of a horse, and Bridget (who called him 'Woody') was devoted to him. At the last open ditch he must have had a heart attack, as he never lifted a leg and fell heavily, along with a couple of the other runners. I was pretty badly shaken by the fall, but more by the sight of the screens going up around old Woody. Next to me in the ambulance was a concussed Welshman who was in no fit state to appreciate the condition of Compton Lad. 'Oh well, boyo,' he chimed in, 'it's all a bit of fun, isn't it?' Not just then it wasn't.

Fred Winter had taken me to Ascot that day, and, aware that he did not like hanging around after racing, I told him that I'd get a lift back to Lambourn with someone else as I thought I'd better go and have a consoling drink with the horse's owners.

'What do you want to do that for?' he asked grumpily.

You miserable bastard, I thought, and felt the same when we lost Nugent at Kempton Park. Fred had not gone racing that day, and when Ben de Haan (who had ridden the horse) and I went into the kitchen at Uplands on our return from the racecourse he looked up from his cup of tea and barked: 'Don't come in here looking like you're at a bloody funeral.'

In time I came to realise that Fred had forced himself to grow a protective shell. Over the years he had lost so many of his best horses in action – including indisputable greats like Bula, Lanzarote and Killiney – and he knew that if you let it get to you, then you were in trouble. Losing horses of that quality hurt deeply, but you had to find a way of dealing with it or you couldn't carry on. People of the calibre of Fred Winter know that such reverses can't be dwelt on. It doesn't mean they care any the less.

If the loss of Parson's Thorns was a deeply grim episode, the overall picture was even grimmer, and the 1992–3 season was rock bottom.

It was becoming more difficult to make any sense at all of my balance sheet, and I was desperately trying to sell the yard. At one point it looked as if I was about to fall into the dreaded pit of negative equity – when the market has gone so low that selling your property recoups less than your debt – and my accountants suggested that I go into voluntary liquidation. On hearing this, my mother admitted that she had an old-fashioned attitude to things like liquidation, and was adamant that I should keep going if I possibly could. By that stage I had very little perspective left, and found myself not caring what I did.

Offers were coming in for the yard, but they were not enough to bail me out, and I tried to think of ways of selling the house without selling the yard. This might well have solved my problems, but I was advised that the house could not be split from the yard without devaluing both, so that turned out to be no solution.

I don't think I could have got through this period without Miriam. It can't have been much fun for her to have to see her fellow turning up from the stable practically every evening on the verge of tears with all the frustration and desperation, but she was always a tower of strength and support.

There wasn't even any solace to be had from the results. We had the worst season of my career. We were badly short of horses and many of those we did have weren't up to much, as is shown from our end-of-term figures: just seventeen winners over jumps and one on the Flat, and we only managed to send out 101 runners all season.

Naturally there was the occasional glimmer of light. Black Humour cheered us up with three wins, and particularly pleasing was his brilliant defeat of Bradbury Star at level weights over three and a quarter miles at Warwick, which made us think that we might have a Gold Cup horse on our hands. In the event we weren't really to find out, as he fell at Cheltenham, though he probably wasn't good enough anyway.

Black Humour's next race after Cheltenham was the

Perrier Jouet Handicap Chase at Aintree, for which he carried top weight. He set off jumping rather deliberately; halfway down the back straight second time round he was about a fence behind the leaders, and I was contemplating throwing myself out of Peter Bromley's BBC radio commentary box at the top of the stand. But then Brad got Black Humour jumping better and he began to eat into the deficit – with the result that they took the lead between the last two fences and ran on to win quite easily.

Never has there been a better example of why, if your jockey has a functioning brain – and Brad certainly had that – you shouldn't pin him down to orders. Our original idea had been for Black Humour to jump off sharpish and make the running, but if Brad had stuck to that notion he would have gone far too fast (a very tempting thing to do round that course at Aintree) and would have fallen in a heap. As it was, Brad knew better, and was rewarded for his patience.

Of course, had something gone wrong halfway through the race the owners' friends would have been quick to point out that Brad wasn't trying, that a bookmaker friend of theirs had said that there was no money for the horse, and all the usual crap. A jockey with a brain and the intelligence to act on his own initiative – and no jockey fits that description more than Brad – will always be open to criticism.

We put that season behind us and faced up to the next, and in the early weeks of autumn 1993 we had a real purple patch, with ten winners from our first eleven runners, including two in France: Bokaro at Clairefontaine and Auteuil.

To keep the costs down for our trip to Clairefontaine, Brad and I decided to go down in his car, but as neither of us much liked driving we persuaded my friend Bruce Urquhart to drive us, with the added bonus that he'd provide a little extra competition on the golf course at Deauville. On our arrival we decided that the Hotel Golf would be nice and handy, but it was stretching the budget a bit for all three of us to have rooms there, so I thought we'd be able to get away with having just one. (Bruce said he was happy to sleep in the bath.) This scheme would work out fine as long as we kept a reasonably low profile and didn't all present ourselves in the lobby for the key at the same time. The plan, though, fell into jeopardy after Bruce made friends with the hotel's assistant manager, through whom he learned that the actor Omar Sharif was staying at the hotel. It was public knowledge that Omar Sharif liked a bet, and, thinking that he could be a useful man to get to know, I sent him a note:

Dear Mr Sharif
    We have a horse running at Clairefontaine in two days' time. He will win. Would you care to have lunch with myself and my patron Lady Joseph at Siro's before racing?
Yours
Charles Brooks

Having put out the bait, I was a bit disappointed not to hear from him the next day. But that evening we were tucking into our dry Martinis and playing table tennis in the hotel bar when who should walk in but Omar Sharif.

He saw Bruce at the bar and slipped along sideways, like an agile crab, to get next to him.

'Monsieur Brooks?' he enquired, without moving his lips or looking sideways.

'Er, no: I'm his private secretary.'

'Please inform Mr Brooks that I am already lunching with friends but I would like to have a drink with Lady Joseph at the races. You really think your horse will win?'

'Oh yes,' said Bruce, 'absolutely certain. Steering job, old boy.'

And with that he was gone.

At the racecourse that day we had bumped into Peter Chapple-Hyam. Over a good lunch he assured us that Oakmead could not be beaten. She was. That reverse, along with the failure of Bruce's fail-safe blackjack system in the casino, had depleted our funds.

The next day we met Lady Joseph for lunch down near the beach and arrived at the course in good time for our race. We found a table on the terrace – and sure enough, sitting further up the terrace, there was Omar Sharif.

'Ooh, Granny!' chirped Lady Joseph's granddaughter. 'There's Omar Sharif! I must go and get his autograph.'

'No, no, don't do that,' I suggested. 'He's an old friend of ours: he'll probably come over and wish us good luck in a minute.'

Omar got up to have a bet. 'Don't let us down,' I muttered under my breath – and he didn't. He came over and charmed everyone in our party. The connection had been made.

Bokaro made all and won by thirty lengths. The French could never quite understand the idea of a horse making the running, yet Clairefontaine is a great track for front-runners. I didn't have a bet – I don't really have the gambling mentality, being too mean – but Omar looked after the race as if he'd had his brains on Bokaro, and there was no question this time about whether he was going to join our table. The champagne started flowing and as we drank it he ordered more. What a grateful punter!

Then, just before the last race, he bade us farewell and departed – and just as we were about to leave ourselves the head waiter appeared with the bill for the champagne.

Perhaps not such a grateful punter after all – but of course Lady Joseph paid the bill with a smile.

Omar Sharif had been worth every bottle of it. A real star.

W e also won two important early-season chases in 1993: the Mercedes-Benz at Chepstow with Espy and the Charisma Gold Cup at Kempton Park with Black Humour, who at last was beginning to get his act together and build into the really good horse we knew he was capable of becoming. Perhaps things were not going to be so bad after all.

The feeling of guarded optimism around the yard was increased by the arrival of a very significant new owner: Madeleine Lloyd Webber, wife of Andrew. The Lloyd Webbers had bought Black Humour on the death of David Bott, and his first race in Madeleine's colours was the 1993 Hennessy Gold Cup at Newbury. He went off 7–2 favourite, and although there wouldn't be many people in the world more pessimistic than me – as a merchant of gloom, I'm right up there with the greats like the late Tim Forster – I really believed Black Humour would win. At the fifth last, the 'cross' fence before the turn into the straight, he was still running away with Brad and looked a certainty, but it's an awkward obstacle on a slightly downhill stretch of the course and he met it all wrong, giving it a tremendous clout and practically breaking the fence in half. It was a wonder he didn't fall; the mistake completely knocked the stuffing out of him and he could never quite get back into the race, but even then he finished only five and a half lengths behind the winner Cogent. Black Humour was very sore and bruised after the race, and I was not the only one who knew that had he not made that blunder he'd have hacked up.

I've never taken a defeat so badly in my life. Before the Hennessy I'd had it in mind to take Black Humour to the jumping guru Yogi Breisner as he was prone to make the odd howler, but then I started to think that he was getting his jumping act together and decided not to bother. Now, after the race, I blamed myself. The Hennessy had slipped from my grasp on account of one jumping error, and I was furious with myself. All that night I sat on the kitchen floor staring at the fridge door and crying with anger. I refused to go to bed and just sat there, hitting myself as hard as I could and every now and then getting up so that I could stamp my feet in fury.

The mood passed, as all moods do, and despite that setback by the beginning of December I still had the best strike rate of winners to runners in the trainers' table.

But yet again the usual pattern came back to haunt me – we'd make a good start, and then the horses would get sick and it would all go pear-shaped again. Apart from our good novice chaser Couldnt Be Better winning a valuable race at Ascot in April 1994, a season that had promised so much and begun so well failed to deliver.

There were no two ways about it. I had to sell Uplands to relieve myself of the crippling financial burden it now presented, and I started talking to potential buyers. One was John Boulter, with whom I got on very well and who turned out to share one of my greatest passions: *The Archers*. I've been a secret admirer of Debbie Aldridge for years and at one time was quite in love with her, since she possessed three of the characteristics that I most admire in a woman: she has an incredibly sexy voice, she's a fearless rider, and she drives a tractor. It's always surprised me that she's never got married, and I suppose she's so busy with the farm now that she simply hasn't the time.

John Boulter asked Miriam and me to meet him one evening in Cirencester, where he revealed that he had a surprise for us: imagine my excitement when he told us that we were going to the Archers' Annual Dinner in Birmingham!

It was a magical occasion. I sat next to John Archer, who was exactly as I'd imagined him – how they could kill him off I'll never know – but the highlight of my night was having a couple of pints with Eddie Grundy (which needless to say I had to pay for). He had dark hair, which surprised me: surely he was blond on the radio?

'Er, Eddie – is Debbie here tonight?'

'No, she couldn't make it. I think she's gone out with someone in Borchester.'

I tried not to look too disappointed, though I was pretty sure she must have been out with one of those bastards from Borchester Land that her father Brian had got involved with.

It was a heady evening, and I felt guilty when later I abandoned my negotiations with John Boulter – which by then were fairly advanced – and ran off over the horizon with someone else. It was the sort of shitty thing that Simon Pemberton would have done.

Back in the real world, there was reason to be optimistic about the following season. On my thirty-first birthday, 3 March 1994, I was phoned by one of the biggest new owners on the National Hunt scene and asked if I could take twenty horses for him. I agreed, and those horses and their owner were to have a very considerable effect on the next four years of my life.

His name was Andrew Cohen.

5

COHEN . . .
COHEN . . .
GONE!

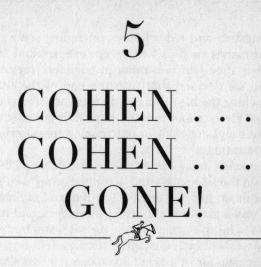

So it was that in the summer of 1994 I sold Uplands to Andrew Cohen, who had made his fortune through the kitchen goods company Betterware and had long had horses in training, most recently with John Upson as his trainer. The arrangement was that I would stay on as a salaried employee of Uplands Bloodstock Ltd and train the horses, and I felt very fortunate that someone had found me (as opposed to me finding them) who was willing both to buy the place from me and to leave me there – and give me the necessary financial backing.

The consignment of Andrew Cohen's horses which came to Uplands in March 1994 was a mixed bunch of youngsters and older horses (including some quite familiar names such as Very Very Ordinary and Zeta's Lad), but they had one thing in common: they were sick. So we decided that with the end of the season approaching the best thing to do was turn them out to grass for three or four months, hope they got over their afflictions and not think about training them seriously until the autumn.

In the event some came back to health, some didn't, but again the season started brightly. For my own part, I was a much happier bunny. The removal of financial worry was a great weight off my shoulders, and it was so good to be able again to go to the sales and buy some nice horses without constantly fretting about how they could be paid for. We didn't go mad, but it was a lovely feeling to be able to go to the sale ring and know that, within reason, I could buy what I wanted more often than not.

Sadly the closing months of 1994 brought the loss of two of the greatest patrons and allies Uplands had known. Bill Tulloch, owner of My Young Man, died in December aged sixty-six, and in November we were suddenly hit by the death of Lady Joseph, who despite her last-minute withdrawal from our planned joint purchase of Uplands had been a wonderful friend and supporter to me throughout my training career. People like Lady Joseph and Bill Tulloch were irreplaceable.

On the racing front, though, good things started to happen. Sound Reveille, a gelding I trained for Angela Abecassis (a great patron of the Guv'nor's and a lady who had given me a big chance when we bought Welsh Bard), was looking very impressive and promised great things, if – like My Young Man before him – a bit hair-raising in his approach to his obstacles. Home-bred, he was a horse to die for. And Dick Whittle's Couldnt Be Better was beginning to look like a very serious racehorse.

Sue and Gerard Nock had bought a horse to fill the void left by the shattering loss of Parson's Thorns. A grey gelding by Roselier, he had taken a long time to come to hand and gained much benefit from the attentions at Uplands of Johnny Cullen, who had been with Fred Winter for many years and put a great deal of time and patience into educating the Nocks' new acquisition. Sue and Gerard decided to name their new pride and joy after Victor Barclay (of Jack Barclay, the Rolls-Royce dealer in Berkeley Square), who after he had been sunning himself for a while was famous among his friends for taking on the complexion of a beetroot: hence the horse's name, Senor El Betrutti. He won a novice hurdle for us at Windsor in November, and at the end of that season Sue told me that she was going to start training herself from their farm near Stow-on-the-Wold, and that the Senor would be leaving us.

This was a very severe setback, as he was clearly a horse of huge potential, and I tried everything I could think of to hang on to him. I offered to buy him, but that was declined. I offered to train him for nothing up front, taking his fees from any prize money won. All to no avail. At that stage Uplands needed the loss of Senor El Betrutti like it needed a hole in the head, and when he left I felt very sorry for Johnny Cullen, who had done wonders with a far from straightforward horse but who would not be around for the big races the grey was bound to win.

In the event Sue – aided no little by Graham Bradley – did a marvellous job with Senor El Betrutti, sending him out to win many big races – including the rare double of the two big two-and-a-half-mile chases at Cheltenham in the autumn of 1997, the Murphy's Gold Cup and the Tripleprint Gold Cup – and seeing him become one of the most popular horses in training. It's perfectly possible that he would not have had such success had he stayed at Uplands – we might have aimed him at different targets, for example, or he might have fallen foul of our pervasive sickness – but for a good while every decent race he won was a painful reminder to us of what we had made and what we had lost. As the years went by that awful feeling of regret wore off, but it hurt at the time.

My first winner in Andrew Cohen's colours – royal blue, white star, white stars on royal blue sleeves and cap – came in a three-mile-one-furlong novice chase at Towcester on 23 November 1994 with a rather slow-looking grey horse called Suny Bay. A gelding by Senor El Betrutti's sire Roselier, Suny Bay had been bought in Ireland from Tom Costello. Like a lot of Tom's horses he didn't have a swanky pedigree but he could do the job, and he was yet another glowing tribute to Tom's skills: not only does he teach his young horses very well, he is a stockman and knows the importance of feeding young horses properly when they are developing.

Suny Bay had been going well enough at home and we weren't exactly amazed that he won at Towcester – his first time over fences – but at that stage we had no inkling that within four years he would have made himself a household name, a horse whose name would be bracketed with those of two other famous greys, Desert Orchid and One Man.

Suny Bay won his next two races – at Towcester again, and then at Warwick, beating the useful Smith's Band. But I was worried about his legs: they felt like lumpy porridge, and I couldn't help feeling that he was always on the verge of breaking down. After Ascot the Sun Alliance was still on the agenda, but such was the condition of the horse's legs that I was worried about how he'd come down the hill at Cheltenham, and doing so under pressure second time round may well have done for him. He was, after all, a young horse, and there would be plenty of time for him to make his mark. But run him now and we might ruin him.

Andrew Cohen was desperate to have a serious contender in one of the big Cheltenham races during his first year as the supremo of Uplands, but somehow I managed to convince him that it would do Suny Bay no good at all: Cheltenham was an accident waiting to happen. We agreed that the horse should be fired and then put away for the rest of the season. (What we used to do in such cases is turn horses out on the side of a hill so that by walking up and down they would be stretching the treated tendons and thus performing their own physiotherapy.)

Firing is a veterinary practice highly unpalatable to many people who are not familiar with it, but for trainers it is an important way of strengthening suspect legs in horses. To stimulate increased blood supply to injured tendons and help them heal, the skin around those tendons is seared with a hot iron (these days usually electrically heated) under local anaesthetic. No doubt it sounds barbaric, but the horse feels no discomfort if dosed up with sufficient painkillers after the anaesthetic wears off. The surest sign that a horse is distressed is if it declines to eat its food, and by and large horses eat up after being fired.

Performed in conjunction with cutting the high check ligament behind the knee to take pressure off the tendon, firing was certainly the best treatment we used for problems in that area of the leg, which are very common in jumpers. To those vets who disapprove of firing (and who a few years ago had it outlawed for a while), we say: come up with a more successful method and we'll use it.

The horses Andrew had brought into the yard did not exactly set the world alight that first season, but that was hardly surprising. The older ones were mostly past their best, and the younger ones that he had bought needed time. So he had to learn that most crucial of virtues in a racehorse owner: patience.

Although Suny Bay didn't make it, Uplands did have one winner at the 1995 Cheltenham Festival in the shape of Sound Reveille, whose victory in the Grand Annual Chase was really a triumph for arnica. Kevin 'Chuck' Norris, the yard's main travelling head lad, always gave the horses arnica before and after their races to stop them getting stiff or bruised should they hit a fence hard or fall. In the Arkle Chase on the Tuesday, the opening day of the Festival, Sound Reveille had been bowling along in the lead when he made such a desperate mistake at the open ditch on the far side that he lost all chance. Once Brad realised that the cause was hopeless he quickly pulled the horse up, and as he walked Sound Reveille back in he looked at me and said: 'Oh dear, Charles, that was a pity. He gave me a great feel.' Then he added: 'He's in the Grand Annual on Thursday.'

'Yes, I know,' I said in a rather surly manner. 'I entered him.'

It is by no means unheard of for a horse to run twice during the three days of the Cheltenham National Hunt Festival, but it's fairly unusual, and with most horses the effort of running in one race, win or lose, is quite enough. But Sound Reveille was clearly so well in himself that it was worth contemplating bringing him out two days after the Arkle: so much depended on how he was the day following that race.

On the Wednesday morning he was a bit sore but generally OK, so we decided to give it a go – and Sound Reveille led most of the way to record a great victory. Without the arnica I'm sure he would have been too bruised to run.

The other great highlight of that season was a funny little four-year-old horse named Aardwolf. He was bred in the purple – by the Prix de l'Arc de Triomphe winner Dancing Brave out of a Habitat mare – and had come our way from the Irish stable of Michael Kauntze, courtesy of the *Daily Mail* diarist Nigel Dempster and Charles Benson. At home Aardwolf showed us nothing, so I decided to run him in a novice hurdle at Exeter towards the end of April to find out how good he might be, not worrying at all about jeopardising his novice status. Indeed, the way he was working, I was more concerned that Aardwolf might remain a novice for the rest of his life.

We held out few hopes for the horse, so I told Nigel and Charles not to bother flogging all the way down to the West Country to watch him run – and I don't think either of them was very pleased with me when he bolted in at 10–1 in a five-horse race. Charles Benson had been known to have the odd bet and would doubtless have appreciated being on his own horse at those odds, but he never managed to get his hands on me to exact his revenge.

That win scuppered Aardwolf's novice status for the following season, so we had to press on with him as soon as we could: he won again at Stratford and then a third time in Paris before finishing fifth in the top French four-year-old race. (Our trip to Paris for the second of these events was quite an experience. We flew over in a helicopter from Battersea, and although Dean Gallagher must have seen a few sights in his time, high on the list of memorable moments must be Charles Benson returning his wine into the vessel from which it had come, there being no loo on the helicopter.)

All in all, not a bad spring's work.

The 1995–6 season seemed to sum up my career, as well as summing up why my partnership with Andrew Cohen failed. There were moments of great possibility which looked as if they were taking us towards a glittering future, but somehow they never seemed to lead on to fulfilment.

We had a good start (as usual): one marvellous Saturday at the end of November everything came good, and we won the Hennessy Gold Cup at Newbury with Couldnt Be Better and the Fighting Fifth Hurdle at Newcastle with Padre Mio within half an hour of each other. It was a wonderful afternoon, yet it left me with a feeling of guilt, as I had persuaded Graham Bradley to ride Black Humour for the Lloyd Webbers rather than Couldnt Be Better. There was very little between the two horses on form (Black Humour started at 11–2, Couldnt Be Better at 15–2), but Black Humour was not an easy ride whereas the other horse was. Shortly before the race it started to rain like hell, and in soft conditions Black Humour's chance went out of the window. I should have withdrawn him and put Brad, the stable jockey, on Couldnt Be Better, but I didn't.

As it worked out it was highly appropriate that Dean Gallagher, who had ridden a lot of winners for Uplands, should partner our first Hennessy winner, and he rode the perfect race to get Couldnt Be Better home from the subsequent Grand National winner Rough Quest. One characteristic of Dean's career is that he has taken most of the chances which have been put his way, which is not easy when you don't get many chances to start with. He fully deserved that big win, and, typically, Brad was thrilled for him.

Six days later we won a chase at Sandown Park with one of the most interesting inmates of Uplands at that time. Lonesome Glory was one hell of a horse. Trained in the USA by Bruce Miller, he had become one of the best steeplechasers ever to race over there, and by the time he came to us to be prepared for a tilt at some of the top races in Britain he had already been voted winner of the Eclipse Award in the States three times, an amazing achievement. He'd won most of the big American steeplechases, including the Colonial Cup in South Carolina twice, and in December 1992 had been sent across to Cheltenham to run in one of the races which formed part of the Sport of Kings Challenge – where he became the first ever American-trained horse to win a jumping race in England.

Lonesome Glory arrived at Uplands towards the end of 1995 and we mapped out a campaign which, if all went well, would lead towards the big races in the spring, possibly even the Gold Cup. The first step on the way was a four-runner handicap chase at Sandown Park in December, and he turned in a terrific performance to beat Egypt Mill Prince and King Credo. So far, so good; but when we then ran him in the Peter Marsh Chase at Haydock in January he was very disappointing, finishing well back. We didn't run him again. I was worried that softer ground than he was used to encountering at home might not have suited him. He was ridden by Blythe Miller, Bruce's daughter, and although she rode him very well she was very light, which meant that he was being asked to hump loads of lead in his saddle-cloth in the big races, and this didn't suit him.

It was decided that in the circumstances the bold idea of bringing him over was not going to be rewarded with the success it deserved, and Lonesome Glory, along with Blythe Miller and Trish who looked after the horse, returned to the USA after just two races for us. Their professionalism made a big impression on us and we were very sorry to see them go – and none of us could quite take it in when we heard not long afterwards that Trish had been killed in a tractor accident on their farm.

Suny Bay came back after a break of ten months to win first time out at Towcester, and we went for one of our raids at Cagnes-sur-Mer with Padre Mio and Garolo, both owned by the Lloyd Webbers. Unfortunately Padre Mio had an off day, so Andrew, Madeleine and I decided to return to England, leaving Brad in France to partner Garolo the following day.

Garolo was narrowly beaten in a photo finish, and after the result was announced Brad was dejectedly walking out of the weighing room after changing when he was cheerily greeted by an English punter: 'If I were you, cock, I'd go and look at the photo. You've been done, pal!'

Brad wandered back in: 'Monsieur – *la photo*, please!'

No response, so he did what most English people in foreign parts do when they're not being understood: he repeated his request, much more loudly.

After a while a steward arrived with the photo – and sure enough, Garolo had won by a head.

Brad's angry enquiry 'What's going on?' caused a miraculous transformation in the steward's linguistic skills. Suddenly he could speak English.

'Monsieur, we have made a mistake. We will have to change the result' – and with that he gave a shrug of his Gallic shoulders and made himself scarce.

All part of the service that we'd got used to over the years.

The new year brought nothing but trouble. Suny Bay appeared to be a steering job in the Mildmay Cazalet Chase at Sandown Park early in January, but tripped up turning into the back straight. I was convinced he'd have won, but to make matters worse, as he struggled to get up he was kicked in the head by another horse and broke his jaw. It was lucky that it wasn't the end of him, but it was a severe setback none the less. And to compound a day of misfortune for Andrew Cohen, two of his other horses ran badly. After the second of these had been defeated Andrew and his gang left the racecourse without coming to see the horse after the race or saying goodbye to us, which I thought rather strange behaviour, and this very minor matter proved to be the first crack in our relationship.

The rest of that season is best not talked about, although Suny Bay eventually recovered from his nasty experience at Sandown Park and after weeks and weeks on the treadmill and in our new swimming pool won the Brown Chamberlin Chase – named for one of the best chasers Fred Winter trained – at Newbury. The swimming pool that aided Suny Bay's recovery was just one of the many spanking new facilities which Andrew Cohen, true to his promise that he would make Uplands a state-of-the-art training facility, had built at huge expense: he also put in indoor horse-walkers and private all-weather gallops.

We ended the season with twenty-nine winners plus three in France and two in Ireland. That total was just about OK, but we needed to up our game to keep Andrew happy, and the young horses had to start coming through.

Early the following season it looked as if that was exactly what was about to happen. Country Star, a bonny little horse that Prince Fahd Salman had sent to me, won at Clairefontaine (where by now the local punters were beginning to latch on to us, so the fancy odds were no longer available), and things started to look up for Andrew. Mywend's, the most expensive of the original batch that he had bought at Doncaster sales, had finally matured and won on his hurdles debut at Uttoxeter in November. He was really beginning to look like a class act, and we sent him to Ascot for his next race later the same month. With Brad riding, Mywend's struck through his tendon, damaging himself irreparably. He had to be put down.

It was at this stage that I started to become aware of murmurings that Brad was not a lucky influence, but I'd never been one to give much credence to that sort of talk, and I put it out of my mind and concentrated on preparing the campaign for the horse who had become the star of the stable, Suny Bay.

During the summer I had persuaded Andrew and the vets to give Suny Bay a general anaesthetic in order to cut the high check ligaments behind his knees. Although he had raced only three times the previous season I was still worried that he wasn't going to stand up to hard work and to racing, and this operation would give him a better chance of coping with the rigours we had in store for him. When he did eventually run at Kempton he did poorly: clearly it was going to take a while to get him right.

Andrew was having the worst period of his whole time at Uplands to date, and somewhat to my consternation his response to this situation was to go over to Ireland and buy five more horses without telling me that he was going – and if that wasn't a vote of no confidence in me then I don't know what it was. Worse still, I genuinely didn't like any of the horses he returned with, though Route One later turned out to be a very good horse.

Hoh Warrior was a lovely young horse that we had

bought from Tom Costello in Ireland and sold on to Bob Michaelson and David Allport, but on the whole people were wary of buying horses from us in that way as they were suspicious of the reasons why Andrew wasn't keeping them. When Hoh Warrior ran first time out in a novice hurdle on Hennessy Gold Cup day at Newbury in November 1996 I told his owners that although I was hopeful I really didn't expect too much, since the opposition included some pretty decent animals and the joint favourite Queen Of Spades looked a good thing. But I assured them that, win or lose at Newbury, Hoh Warrior was a good prospect and could be expected to win next time out. Brad's instructions were simple: hunt him round, try and put him in the race going to the second last, give him a kick in the belly and don't be hard on him.

In the event Brad didn't have to give him that kick in the belly: it was some debut, Hoh Warrior winning easily at 50–1. Luckily, in spite of my lack of confidence David Allport had followed his usual habit of putting a few quid on his runner, and had Hoh Warrior in a forecast with Queen Of Spades, who was second. David made a good few quid, though no one in the yard had had a penny on the horse.

After the race I went into the gents' in the Members' Enclosure and was having a quick pee when two big blokes came and stood next to me.

Big Bloke One: 'That bloody Brooks and Bradley had it off again in the last.'

Big Bloke Two: 'Yeah. Hasn't that fucker Brooks got the sort of face you'd like to hit?'

I decided not to wait to 'adjust my dress' and was

out of there like a shot. People like that never cease to amaze me. If only we were as clever as they seem to think we are, we wouldn't be peeing in the same country as them.

Although we still weren't having enough winners, Couldnt Be Better won the Thyestes Chase at Gowran Park in Ireland, and in February 1997 a flying machine named Double Symphony pulled off the unusual feat of winning two top-class races under different codes – the Agfa Hurdle at Sandown Park and the Game Spirit Chase at Newbury – on successive Saturdays. She was a difficult mare to train, but she was the most impressive work horse I had ever known, with the possible exception of Barton.

It was an open secret that things were not going as smoothly at Uplands as they might have been, and for the last year rumours had been hanging over my head that I was about to get the sack. During the build-up before Suny Bay's next race, the Greenalls Grand National Trial at Haydock Park in February, these rumours got louder, and according to some people who claimed to be in the know they were not rumours but fact. As far as I was concerned there were no two ways about it: if Suny Bay did not win the Grand National Trial, I was on my way. Andrew had not said anything but he didn't really need to: I could see which way the wind was blowing.

Suny Bay had bled a bit after his Kempton race, and as Haydock approached we knew we had to be careful with him. Fast work increases the number of red blood cells, while long steady work reduces it, which means that the blood of a horse kept on long steady work is thinner: thus that horse is less susceptible to bleeding as the capillaries are not subjected to intense stress. In addition, the horse's lungs are put under less exertion during day-to-day training and so will not be liable to bleed while working. Exercising Suny Bay steadily twice a day proved a very effective way of getting him back to the track without damaging his lungs.

We had two runners in the Grand National Trial, Suny Bay and our Hennessy winner Couldnt Be Better, which again presented a dilemma for our stable jockey Graham Bradley. In the Agfa Hurdle I had offered Brad the choice of Florid (owned by Lord Howard de Walden) or Double Symphony (owned by the Lloyd Webbers), with a heavy hint that Lord Howard would expect the stable jockey to be on his horse, whereas the others would be quite happy with Jamie Osborne. When it came to the Haydock Park race, I told Brad that it was entirely up to him. His view was that Couldnt Be Better was working very well at home and that Suny Bay was not fit enough to do himself justice. Without making too big a deal of it, I suggested to Brad that if he got off the grey I could not see him getting back on him, and the Grand National itself was on the horizon. He followed his own judgement and elected to ride Couldnt Be Better.

That day at Haydock was pretty tense. I was driven up to the racecourse by Spud, a former box driver, and on the way up he told me, with some authority, that the word in Lambourn was that if Suny Bay didn't win then I would be out and Noel Chance, who trained in Lambourn not far from Uplands, would be in.

Brad had picked wrong – for once it wasn't my fault – and Suny Bay, ridden by Jamie Osborne, hacked up, with Couldnt Be Better a distant fourth. As I left the racecourse Spud was waiting in the car, and greeted me with the words: 'Well, that's fucked Noel Chance.'

Suny Bay was Jamie's eighth chance ride for me that season, and his seventh winner – and three of those were owned by Andrew. If the owner of Uplands were thinking of a change in jockey arrangements, you wouldn't need to be a genius to work out in which direction he'd be thinking.

I had my own views on the situation and I shared them with Andrew, but it was clear to me that, at the end of the day, whatever I felt I would be overruled. As far as Andrew was concerned, Brad had been unlucky – maybe through no fault of his own, but he had been unlucky, and Andrew believed very strongly in luck. For that reason he wanted to leave Jamie on Suny Bay for the Grand National. I have always been a great believer in loyalty, and I was adamant that Brad was the stable jockey and as long as that was the case there could be no question that he should ride the horse. Had a similar situation arisen with a trainer such as Fulke Walwyn the owner would have been thrown out of the yard; but it's quite difficult to take such a position if that owner also owns the yard!

It's hard to say that one of us was right and one was wrong, but it did show that by now Andrew and I were coming from completely different directions.

The story of the extraordinary 1997 Grand National – complete with the bomb scare, the heroism of Suny Bay's lad Phil Sharpe, and a message to C. Brooks from the Merseyside constabulary to return their property by six o'clock that evening, or else – is told elsewhere in this book. Suffice it to say now that Jamie rode Suny

Bay in the National when it was eventually run on the Monday following Saturday's postponement, and the horse turned in a marvellous performance to finish second behind the brilliant winner Lord Gyllene. Jamie gave him a great ride.

Brad rode Lo Stregone for Tom Tate, and they pulled up.

In February 1997 I ended up in the Wellington Hospital. An infection which had set in following surgery on my knee the previous year was not going away, and further serious surgery was deemed necessary. This was a bloody nuisance, but the great thing about being in hospital in London is that people can drop in all the time, and I was rarely lacking visitors.

Nigel Dempster sent round caviar. Michael Jackson (paper rather than pop) brought me plenty of champagne, and the members of the Bow Lane Partnership, a syndicate of owners for whom I trained the laziest horse in England in the shape of Strokesaver, came for an all-night party: they even had to pop out to the off-licence to reload. At least while they were drinking in my hospital room I could sell them the odd horse, and Danny and Caroline Bell left the hospital one day as proud owners of a share in The Full Monty.

The nurses in the Wellington didn't quite understand what I meant when I announced one day that I was going to put a few quid for them on Florid at Fakenham. They assumed I meant over the phone, but I didn't.

Before I'd checked in to the Wellington I'd discovered the location of the nearest betting shop, about half a mile from the hospital, and when about three days after the operation I was allowed up on crutches, I'd casually suggested, as the nurse and I had passed the back staircase (for use only in emergencies), that perhaps I should soon try steps. Everything was falling into place for the Great Escape the next day.

Half an hour before Florid was due to run I slipped on what clothes I could, checked nobody was around and ducked down the back stairs, through the rear exit and out into St John's Wood High Street. I hobbled along to the betting shop and went inside. A few of the punters seemed a bit surprised to see me half clothed, half still in my pyjamas, but those who recognised me took my miraculous appearance in their midst as a sign from above, and were happy enough when Florid, with 'Muppet' Berry doing well not to fall off, duly obliged at 3–1. I hobbled back to the Wellington, and no one there was any the wiser.

A week later I repeated the operation to see Hisar run in a novices' hurdle at Newbury. He was a fat and stuffy horse, and I confidently informed the incumbents of the betting shop that he would need the race that day and was not to be backed. If he hadn't kicked the second last hurdle out of the ground he would have won rather than finished second at 7–1, and as I was in no position to leg it down St John's Wood High Street pursued by angry punters, I was relieved that he didn't.

This time the nurses had discovered my escape, and they took a very dim view of it, assuring me that they'd all be fired if the doctors found out, etc. A bit like Douglas Bader in *Reach For The Sky*, I was deprived

of my crutches, and that was the end of my visits to
William Hill.

While I was in hospital the dreaded Strokesaver ran
like a goat under Dean Gallagher at Fontwell and two
weeks later won with Muppet at Wincanton. Neither
event was particularly remarkable, except for the fact
that two years later the Serious Crime Squad went to
question the Bow Lane Partnership to try to establish
whether they'd had a coup. To be frank, if I made a list
of the horses I handled in my time as a trainer which I
would *not* want to try and have a coup with, Strokesaver
would come pretty near the top.

In the summer of 1997 we instigated a scheme whereby
the young and backward horses would go to David
Foster and his wife Sneeze in Ireland to spend a year
or so being brought along, possibly running in the odd
point-to-point, before being returned to Uplands for the
serious business of racing. David, who had ridden in the
Irish three-day-event team at the Atlanta Olympics, was
an exceptional horseman, and I was all for this idea, as
it got the backward babies out of my hair at Uplands
and meant that David could filter out the wheat from the
chaff: the best horses would come to us, the other ones
we would get rid of through a third party (ideally to some
unsuspecting English trainer). After meeting the Fosters
I was even keener on the idea, as they were such talented
but straightforward people that I was hugely looking
forward to working with them. For a start we sent them
about twenty young horses together with a few yearlings
and two-year-olds who had been hanging around in the
paddocks at Uplands, feeding on very immature pasture.

I was sure that our yard would be healthier without all those snotty-nosed coughing babies around us creating a pool of infection.

The horses that came back to us from 'Operation Foster' produced mixed results. Those that I'd bought at Tattersalls' Derby Sale at Fairyhouse were more promising and were to do better than those Andrew had acquired without me (I would have been appalled if it had been any different, given the contrast between my racing knowledge and experience and his), and two which particularly pleased me were Wood Hall and Captain Dee Cee, named after David Foster himself. I had left Uplands by the time they appeared on a racecourse but I followed their progress with great interest. Captain Dee Cee won a bumper at Exeter in a highly promising fashion; Wood Hall won his bumper at Ascot, but subsequently had a very bad bout of colic and died. It must have been a desperate blow for the yard to lose such a prospect.

What would prove to be my last season at Uplands, the 1997–8 term, started well enough. Especially encouraging was our strength in the novice chaser department: Hoh Warrior, Raleagh Native, Shekels and Wilde Music all looked as if they could win at the top tracks.

Brad had introduced me to Raleagh Native's owner Michael Jackson – who also owned 1991 Champion Hurdler Morley Street – and his wife Nita, and had tipped me off that they weren't very keen on bad behaviour. I don't suppose I made a very good impression on them (I certainly didn't on Miriam) when I arrived for a 'let's get to know each other' dinner at Harry's Bar in London one evening after I had been to the lunch sponsored by Martell to mark publication of the 1998 Grand National weights. To say I was well refreshed might have been an understatement – after the Martell lunch I'd spent three hours in the bar with fellow trainers Nigel Twiston-Davies and Kim Bailey – and when I arrived for dinner at Harry's Bar I was greeted by Miriam with one of her special 'I'd like to smack you very hard but I won't because you'll never get up' looks. I did a pretty good job of sobering up during dinner, drinking plenty of water, but then Michael asked me if I'd like to try the melon grappa: God! it was good, and I enjoyed the end of the bottle as much as I had the beginning.

Despite Brad's warning, Michael did not seem unduly put out by my performance that evening, and invited us along with Jamie Osborne and his girlfriend Katie O'Sullivan to a party near Salehurst in East Sussex a few weeks later. This would involve a serious amount of driving, and Jamie came up with a great idea: we'd get a camper van and hire a driver. That way we could sleep, drink, play cards, etc. and travel in style. Jamie nipped round to the second-hand camper van place in Lambourn, picked one out and asked if he could take it home that night to show his girlfriend, hoping that the owner wouldn't check the mileage on its return. We found a driver, and the plan worked a treat – except that, not being very experienced in the ways of camper vans, we had not allowed for the fact that at fifty miles an hour flat out it was going to take us an hour longer to get to the Jacksons' party than we'd anticipated. We eventually got there, but the rest of the gathering were halfway through their main course as we entered, and I'd managed to drop my dinner jacket in the mud as we'd got out of the camper van, so I looked pretty dishevelled. Good way to make a really bad impression.

Sadly, Michael Jackson died in July 1999.

How surprised would I have been if I'd been told in the autumn of 1997 that I was about to embark on my last season at Uplands?

At Andrew Cohen's insistence, Jamie was now Suny Bay's jockey, but a couple of days before he was due to ride the grey in his first race of the season, the Edward Hanmer Chase at Haydock Park, he smashed his wrist when coming off Space Trucker at Cheltenham: it was a very bad break, and had it happened ten years earlier I doubt he would have kept his hand. So, from being on the verge of giving up when Andrew Cohen had jocked him off Suny Bay the previous season, Brad now found himself back on the grey horse.

The original plan had been to go straight for the Hennessy at Newbury rather than Haydock, since we had managed to get Suny Bay very fit and I thought he could win it without a prep race. But a couple of days before the entries for the Edward Hanmer closed I walked the course at Newbury and was appalled to find the take-off and landing sides of the fences very firm – they had probably been compacted – and the rest of the course riding good to firm. Having spent months getting the horse ready for the Hennessy, it now looked as if we wouldn't be able to run him unless there was a huge amount of rain, which was not the forecast. In the circumstances we thought we'd better give him a run at Haydock, where the ground was safe, though if he won there he'd get a four-pound penalty for the Hennessy and have been subjected to a race we didn't want him to have.

There was general concern about the state of the going at Newbury in the period leading up to the Hennessy. Other trainers were going ballistic, yet when I reflected their views to the *Sporting Life* by way of explanation as to why Suny Bay probably wouldn't run in the big race, the back-up I got from the others was very disappointing. Behind closed doors they had very strong feelings, but when it came to standing up and being counted most of them were heading over the horizon with their arses on fire. It is perfectly understandable that they don't want to upset other people in the industry, but that is no recipe for getting things done. On this occasion there was a big row, and within a year £40,000 had been spent on the Newbury track to improve the situation. Of course, there are times when behind-the-scenes diplomacy works better than confrontation, but there are also times when confrontation is the only way forward.

Oblivious to all this fuss, Suny Bay won the Edward Hanmer very well indeed from General Wolfe and See More Business (who would go on to win the 1999 Cheltenham Gold Cup) and looked to have a major chance in the Hennessy, despite that penalty which took his Newbury weight to 11st 8lb.

In the few days leading up to the Hennessy quite a few of our horses ran poorly, and I was beginning to fret that the illness which always seemed to affect us with the approach of winter was going to arrive early. But Suny Bay had come out of his Haydock race very well, and an additional bonus was that it was raining hard – very hard. In fact, the going on the day was getting softer by the minute, and by the time the race arrived I was worried that the weight might become too much of a burden for him in that ground.

Suny Bay took the lead from the start, skipped happily over the first three fences down Newbury's back straight, and then came face to face with disaster. At the fourth fence he made a very uncharacteristic mistake and slammed into the fence with such force that the reins were yanked out of Brad's hands and would have gone over the horse's head had he not had such big ears. Brad made a miraculous recovery, and the rest of the race was pretty plain sailing, with Suny Bay regaining the lead after being given a little time to recover from the shock of that blunder, and just galloping his rivals into the ground. At the line Barton Bank was thirteen lengths behind the grey, which was a good run from David Nicholson's horse, as he wouldn't have liked the ground at all.

That Hennessy day attracted a huge amount of media attention as the race was the last to be called by the 'Voice of Racing', Sir Peter O'Sullevan, and it was a real thrill to win Sir Peter's last race. Like everyone else who has ever heard him in action, I've always loved his commentaries, and it's incredible to think that the BBC have had two such outstanding – and long-standing – front-line commentators as Sir Peter on television and Peter Bromley on radio: different styles for different types of broadcasting, but both highly effective. In Jim McGrath and Lee McKenzie the BBC have managed to find two worthy successors.

Sir Peter shares a birthday with me. On the evening after Couldnt Be Better had won the Hennessy, he very kindly left a message on our answering machine to say how much he enjoyed calling the horse home. I meant to keep the tape for posterity, but forgot to take it out of the machine, and Sir Peter's message was eradicated by a call from the plumber to say that he'd be up to mend the washing machine on Monday.

Uplands had four other runners at Newbury that day and they all pulled up. As Brad came in on the last one, Holly's Pride in the novices' hurdle, he looked at me and said: 'Charles, thank fuck I didn't fall off the old grey bugger, or we'd have had a real bastard of a day.'

Brad riding the winner of the Hennessy for me was a wonderful moment. I could never forget how pleased he had been for Dean Gallagher two years earlier, and I thought it was very unfair for him to have lost the ride on Suny Bay in the first place. Justice had been done.

The celebrations went on for a couple of days. We made it as far as The Bell in Boxford (where we'd stopped for a drink after Couldnt Be Better had won the Hennessy two years earlier) before moving on to The Queen's Arms in East Garston, and finished up the next day in The Hare and Hounds above Lambourn. Andrew Cohen picked up the tab. It has to be said that he was a very generous host. Not only did he have very good wine: he was only too happy too open it.

But once the celebrations were over they were fairly quickly forgotten. The other four horses pulling up at Newbury had been no coincidence. The horses were sick again, and between Hennessy day and 25 February 1998, some three months later, we had just three winners. It was the same miserable business all over again – and to make matters worse, Suny Bay ran in the King George

VI Chase at Kempton, finished fourth behind See More Business and came back all wrong. This was just the first phase of what with hindsight was a disastrous preparation for another attempt at the Grand National.

In 1997 Suny Bay's programme had been ideal: a midwinter break followed by the Greenalls Gold Cup at Haydock, then straight to Aintree. This time round Andrew insisted that the Hennessy had proved Suny Bay one of the best chasers in the land and we should go for the King George and the Gold Cup. This seemed to me to be all wrong for the horse, but I took no satisfaction in his failure at Kempton. On his return from that race he seemed to have pulled muscles in his left hind leg. Fortunately we were employing Madeleine Lloyd Webber's sister Melanie Gurdon as a full-time physiotherapist, and she put a lot of work into his rehabilitation. Even so, his recovery was very slow. In February, with the Gold Cup rapidly approaching, he really had to get back into serious work, but when Simon McNeill took him for a canter one Saturday he reported that the horse felt like a cripple.

As orthodox treatment was not working to schedule, it was time for the unorthodox.

Glenn Hoddle received a good deal of mockery for bringing in Eileen Drewery to help condition the England football squad, but I've always had plenty of time for the notion of healing – years ago I'd felt the benefit myself after sustaining a neck injury in a fall – and called in a healer called John Johnson to come and look at Suny Bay. When he ran his hands over the horse he duly found an injury high on the right foreleg – which is where another physiotherapist, Mary Bromiley, had all along suspected there might be a problem. A horse's legs work in opposite pairs, so it made sense for the right foreleg and left hind leg to be connected. It is always important to remember with horses that they can have more than one injury or weakness – indeed, one will often cause another. John Johnson felt the problem he had identified had responded. The following day Graham Bradley (who did not know about the healer's visit) rode Suny Bay and said he was fine, and we never detected any recurrence of the problem.

Suny Bay was not fit enough to run in the Greenalls and I was never convinced that he could be got straight enough for a realistic bid for the Cheltenham Gold Cup – not that it was in any case a suitable race for him – but Andrew decided that he had to take his chance, so take his chance he did.

What a disaster! Predictably for a horse who excelled on flat tracks such as Newbury or Aintree, he loathed Cheltenham's ups and downs, made a very bad mistake as the pace got hotter on the second circuit and after finishing a distant fifth behind Cool Dawn came back with his hind legs impregnated with gorse from the take-off apron of the fence he'd clobbered. He was in extreme discomfort, and even his devoted lad Phil Sharpe could not get near enough to draw the poisonous pricks out with a poultice. So we had to put him on painkillers and antibiotics, stopping the treatment ten days before the National to avoid failing the dope test.

The idea of getting Suny Bay to Aintree at his peak and mentally ready to run for his life had been blown out the window by running him at Cheltenham, but in the circumstances he ran a fantastic race in the

National. Carrying top weight of twelve stone (twenty-five pounds more than when he had finished runner-up in 1997), he was the only runner who in desperately heavy conditions could keep up with the mud-loving Earth Summit (carrying twenty-three pounds less than him) during the final mile of the race. Going to the last fence the weight started to anchor him, but he stayed on steadfastly to finish second again.

The comments of *Raceform* are worth quoting:

> Suny Bay, who looked magnificent, made a heroic attempt to defy twelve stone. In effect, he was 18lb higher in the ratings than when runner-up behind Lord Gyllene twelve months ago. Given a patient ride, he moved up into contention setting out on to the final circuit and, after a head to head with the winner from four out, the 23lb weight difference took its toll going to the final fence. This was the best weight-carrying performance in the Grand National since Crisp in 1973 and he must now be rated the top staying chaser.

Timeform called Suny Bay's effort 'the best performance in the race in over twenty years and one of the very best of the modern era'.

They were right, of course; but I knew that if he hadn't run at Cheltenham we might well have been saluting the Grand National winner, not just the heroic runner-up.

Suny Bay's gallant failure at Aintree did nothing to paper over the cracks in my relationship with Andrew Cohen, which for several months had been starting to open up like crevasses in a glacier.

For him, there were two basic problems: I wasn't attracting enough horses from other owners, and I wasn't training enough winners. He felt he had thrown a considerable amount of money into the operation (which was undeniable) and he wanted more success.

On the first count, I was doing my level best, although we didn't always agree on tactics. Early on during my time with Andrew we had sent out to all registered owners with more than one trainer a brochure advertising the yard. I felt that this was a waste of time and, worse, would cause bad feeling among other trainers, and although I was right on both counts I had to support and defend Andrew's decision. The mailing provoked a good deal of hypocrisy from other trainers, one of whom sent me a very rude letter despite the fact that he had invited one of our owners to his open day. Sending out that brochure was not, in my opinion, an effective way of marketing ourselves, but I suspect that Andrew interpreted my reluctance as a sign that I wasn't ambitious enough.

One day in January 1998 I further displeased the boss by having a day's shooting with Tim Hoare. I'd met Tim when staying at Manton with the Sangsters, and he told me he'd like to have a horse with me (I think he was impressed by my still being in my dinner jacket at breakfast), so going shooting with him was not bunking off but a legitimate contact with a new owner. Andrew did not see it that way, but as far as I was concerned it was fairly simple. I'd been told I was not getting enough clients, and I tried to explain to Andrew that I was not going to fill the empty boxes at Uplands by sitting on my arse in Lambourn. But Andrew was adamant. He didn't like the idea of my going shooting, and told me that he could make me go racing at Windsor that day. I explained that I had a long-standing invitation with a potential client and that my assistant Simon McNeill would be representing me at Windsor. Our conversation then descended from a discussion into an argument, with him complaining that I didn't seem to be very good at getting other clients and me countering that this was possibly more to do with him than with me.

It would be fair to say that during this conversation our relationship hit an all-time low, and the end was very clearly in sight.

At that time there were about eighty horses in the yard, of which some thirty-five or so belonged to other owners and the rest to Andrew Cohen. It was becoming increasingly obvious to me that it was not an appealing proposition for a prospective owner to have a horse in a yard owned by and obviously dominated by another owner, and it was simply an impossible task to attract enough owners to keep Andrew's figures-men happy.

The second problem was very straightforward: it was difficult to make winners out of horses who were sick, and most of those in the yard were not right.

After winning the Hennessy with Suny Bay the season turned into a nightmare, and that Christmas – a month after the Hennessy – I told my mother and Miriam that I had had enough of training sick horses, some of which were owned by people with whom I did not get on. They persuaded me that it would be unfair on everyone in the yard to leave halfway through the season, and of course they were right. I had to soldier on, but I had no illusions about what lay in store.

On the morning of Easter Monday 1998, nine days after Suny Bay's National heroics, I was summoned into the house at Uplands, where Andrew and his wife Wendy were waiting for me in the sitting room. (I sensed that Wendy wanted to be there to hear the conversation first hand: since my less-than-productive session with Andrew in January, she had done her best to ease the situation behind the scenes and prevent the two of us falling out irreparably.)

I sat down, and the tone of the conversation soon became pretty clear. Andrew was not happy with my personal life, and obviously felt that I wasn't as committed as I should have been to the success of Uplands – which I interpreted as his feeling that if I were pinned down by the financial constraints of a wife and family I would be easier to control. He didn't think I was dedicated enough, and as evidence cited the work I did for BBC radio and my column in the London *Evening Standard* (though I'd always thought of those jobs as trying to promote myself as a trainer, and thus Uplands as a yard).

He then said that it was my fault that the horses were sick in spite of the vast amount he'd forked out for veterinary treatment. (The fact that most of the yards in Lambourn had had a terrible time of it that season was apparently irrelevant.) If I were really ambitious, he declared, I would find a way round the problem.

Finally – to my mind the best accusation of all, from a pretty strong line-up – he said that I had been placing his horses badly. With this I could only agree wholeheartedly. At the beginning of each month he would give me a list of fixtures where his horses could not run as it was not convenient for him. It also tended not to suit him to go and watch just one of his horses race: he'd prefer to have two or three, which tended not to suit the other horses. So yes – I placed the horses badly. But trainers and owners regularly disagree on this matter.

The long and the short of it was that he wanted me to change my character and the way I did my job. Fair enough, he was the boss – but I felt I knew more about the horses than he did and should be allowed to train them in the way I saw fit. (Some of his carping about my methods wouldn't have been so aggravating had I felt that he had more knowledge about horses. You could take that sort of criticism from Sheikh Mohammed, but it comes with less authority from someone with as little experience as Andrew Cohen.) As far as I was concerned, this was not just a question of the passengers flying the plane: they'd pulled the cockpit door off its hinges and were playing with all the switches.

There was only one possible end to that conversation: I said I would leave the yard at the end of the season. We all agreed to keep this news under our hats for the rest of the day; the staff and the owners would have to be told in an organised manner before the press got hold of the story.

After that unpleasant encounter I decided to seek distraction in the beer tent at the Old Berks point-to-point at Lockinge, where I was a spectator at a highly impressive brawl between what can only be described as an Eton and Radley Combined XI and a Wantage XI that, from the look of their bent noses, had had far too much match practice. To my amazement the young blue-bloods got stuck in with some enthusiasm and then managed to execute a tactical withdrawal which left the Wantage XI beating the crap out of a whole load of blokes who (from where I was cowering) looked like they had entered the fray as their allies. I slipped sharply out the rear exit behind the bar and grabbed the first policeman I could find.

'Deaths!' I told him. 'That's what there'll be in there if you don't get in sharpish!'

But the police are not trained to be dead heroes, so this copper wasn't going anywhere until reinforcements arrived, and by now the sides of the beer tent were bulging with bodies, chairs were being smashed over people's heads and there was blood everywhere. I really don't think they need bother with the racing there in future.

By the end of that traumatic Easter Monday events at Uplands had paled into insignificance. In Ireland, David Foster had been killed. Riding a nondescript horse at an innocuous water jump at a small hunter trial, David had fallen and had been killed instantly. I was devastated, and flew out to Dublin the next day. At the funeral, the church was packed. I had been planning to stay outside, but was urged to go into the church, where the only available seat was right up the front, just a couple of yards from the coffin: I whispered to David that if I could have swapped places with him I would have done so.

I couldn't bear to see the faces of David's three young children, who were too young to lose such a lovely father, and I heard the youngest say to Sneeze: 'Mum, this is worse than when the dog died, isn't it?'

It was the saddest moment of my adult life.

After the service I sat on the wall of the churchyard with Lucinda Green, one of the great figures of the eventing world, and, thinking of John Durkan as well as David, we talked of why it was that the best always seemed to go early.

Within a week of being back in England I had to face the practical realities of my decision to leave Uplands.

I took the view that at that stage it would do no one any good were I to air the reasons why I had stood down – Andrew Cohen's massive vote of no confidence – and since I wasn't yet sure about whether or not I'd try to resume my training career I didn't want to be drawn by the press on that matter. In addition, the last thing I wanted was to descend into a slanging match with Andrew Cohen.

On the whole the press seemed to accept this silence – some journalists even took the time to write sympathetic letters – but the one person who didn't seem to think I had the right to keep my own counsel was Channel Four Racing's John McCririck, who in his customary manner demanded an explanation. This attack did not bother me in the slightest – though it did cause Brad to defend me – and it seemed to be entirely typical of John's blustering style.

John McCririck is one of racing's most public faces, but he seems to me to present a paradox. Is he a colourful character who enhances the attractions of racing to a wider public? Or is he a fat, self-promoting, loud-mouthed git who would say anything to attract attention to himself while giving the impression that his life is dedicated to the protection of the ordinary punter?

'Character' or charlatan? I've pondered this great conundrum over the years, and reached the conclusion that he is both. He's very well informed and knowledgeable about certain aspects of racing (though his grasp of the finer points of jockeyship is sometimes tenuous, to say the least) but essentially he is in my view a creation of his own imagination rather than a natural occurrence.

And while on the subject of McCririck, I find it infuriating that he (and a couple of other leading racing journalists) are often sniping at Peter Savill, chairman of the British Horseracing Board. Savill is racing's only hope of extracting a fair deal for racing from the bookmakers, and he's already done more for the sport than anyone else in the recent past (with the possible exception of Lord Hartington). He's abrasive and tough, and at present is exactly the sort of person racing needs to fight its corner. So when I hear McCririck and others criticising Savill I can't help asking myself why they have so taken against him.

My last runner as a trainer was Father Rector in a hunter-chase at Market Rasen on 30 May 1998, and I went out with a winner – as I had started ten years before.

Leaving Uplands was a very sad moment. With the exception of my six months with Nick Gaselee, I had been at the yard since leaving school, and those sixteen years represented, in effect, all my working life.

Financially I was much worse off than when I started my training career, but I didn't really mind that: if money were an overriding factor, not many people would immerse themselves in National Hunt racing. Much worse than the financial position was the knowledge that leaving Uplands was admitting defeat. You can be doing badly at something, but as long as you keep doing it, then you haven't lost. As soon as you stop, you're defeated. But is that a good reason to carry on doing something that doesn't agree with you? When I first broached the idea of giving up, my mother rather exasperatedly told Miriam that I was just like my father, and I was rather pleased by that comparison. Although my father farmed all his life, he was a restless spirit who would probably have liked to take up other challenges if his situation had allowed him to.

My strongest emotion by far on leaving Uplands was the feeling that I was letting people down. Although my mother had initially opposed my going into racing, she had wholeheartedly supported me while I was doing it, buying horses for me to ride and supporting me in countless other ways. And for seven years Miriam had helped me keep going, not just mentally but in practical ways as well: she made a huge contribution to the business by helping entertain owners and going racing. By giving up I was throwing all of their efforts out the window. I was also letting down everyone who worked at Uplands. In the office, Annabel Owen had been with me from the time I took over from Fred, and Jo Russell had become an important member of the team. Now I was walking away from them.

There were the jockeys, too: Graham Bradley, Dean Gallagher, Muppet Berry and our two young riders Carl Rafter and Gary Brace: I hadn't done them any favours. And what about poor old Brian Delaney? I had worked with him since my very first day at Uplands, and at times had turned his life upside down when I was going around changing things, especially when I was madly trying to find some way of stopping the horses getting sick. All that upheaval for nothing. Chuck Norris and Tony McKeown were my two travelling head lads, and I had given them their jobs when they were both quite young. It was as if we had grown up together, and by giving up I had really pulled the rug from under their feet. Still, it was assumed that Andrew would replace me with another trainer at Uplands just as soon as he could find one, and so most of the staff would still have jobs there, while those who wanted to leave would have no difficulty getting positions elsewhere in Lambourn: they were the best group of lads in the village.

The last four years had been a roller-coaster ride. Andrew Cohen had been as good as his word and had let me spend a great deal of his money, and I had not produced the results he had been looking for. At times it had been good fun – especially walking into a sale ring and being able to buy a nice horse without fretting too much about the cost. (Wendy Cohen had once watched us get outbid on two horses in Ireland and said: 'I don't understand what you're doing. If you like a horse, why don't you just buy it?' We paid 65,000 guineas for the next lot – Wood Hall – with one bid.)

If things had been a little different we might have succeeded. To start with, I let Andrew spend too much on non-essentials. He had wanted to buy the yard only if he could buy land with it, yet in the event having hundreds of acres of paddocks and our own gallop proved an unnecessary expense. Other trainers in Lambourn do perfectly well without their own gallops. Nor did we need to have our own swimming pool for the horses. It was handy, of course, but really it was an expensive luxury; as with the gallops and paddocks, the money might have been better spent on horses or just left in the bank.

Our second mistake was to buy too many 'store' horses

– that is, horses you acquire with a view to leaving them to mature for a couple of years before attempting to win races with them. Filling the yard up with babies, however promising they may be, is not the way to succeed, and no serious jumping owner can maintain a high level of achievement when concentrating on buying untried horses. The intake of young horses has to be balanced by the acquisition of some who have proved themselves: running on the Flat, or in point-to-points or bumpers, or over obstacles in France or Ireland. Such horses, however, can be very expensive, and errors are costly; so although we bought the odd horse in this way we set our sights more on the cheaper, untried horse – cheaper, that is, until you've kept it for two years and discovered it's no bloody good!

Top owners like J. P. McManus or David Johnson have shown that money can buy a good team of horses. The mistake we made at Uplands was in spending so much on the infrastructure of the place.

A few days after Father Rector had signed off the Brooks training career – or at least, this particular phase of it – Brian Delaney sent to the *Racing Post* a poem written in my honour by Tony Gilmore, the yard's chiropractor:

> So farewell then to Charlie Brooks, oh stout and
>   well-met fellow
> Goodbye, too, to the polo hat, the coat of rape-
>   flower yellow
> Toodle-pip to the dressing gown that made the
>   national telly
> As you chewed the fat with Inverdale in your jim-

jams and your wellies
Oh sayonara, Charlie-boy, Uplands heaves a sigh
And wipes a sentimental tear from its misty morning eye

Adieu, old friend, the ladies say, and wring their hands or twist 'em
Ta-ta to your well-filled jodhpurs, pal – strange your granddad never missed 'em
Arrivederci Miriam, the beauty to your beast
And peckish dogs, and bottomless cats, the spectres at the feast
Adios those memories, Fahd Salman, remember him?
You got the freedom of his country for teaching Country Star to swim!

So long, C. Brooks, a saddening day, the yard won't be the same
But we'll meet again, there's little doubt, in this strange old racing game
No doubt we'll see you in the press setting sartorial trends
Instead of standing in the yard, your candle lit both ends
Bye bye chum, it's time to go and stop this maudlin piffle
Just p*** off mate and don't look back lest we should start to sniffle.

6

'I DIDN'T REALISE MY HORSE HAD SIX FEET'

A NDREW COHEN MAY HAVE caused me difficulties, but at least he never got me into anything like the situation I found myself in one evening with a very well-heeled and aristocratic owner, who to spare her (and my) blushes I will call Mrs X.

I'd been training in my own right at Uplands for a while, and at the time was pursuing a sixteen-year-old schoolgirl at St Mary's, Ascot, a very useful location for a racehorse trainer, though the beady eye of the authorities meant that the usual place for our trysts was the group of rhododendron bushes in the school grounds. I became very familiar with the rhododendron bushes of Ascot during that period, but the object of my affections soon tired of being pursued by this ancient twenty-eight-year-old, and she gave me the boot.

Shortly afterwards I was summoned by Mrs X, a widow then well into her sixties, to her country estate, supposedly to talk about plans for her horses. It soon became clear, however, that she had other things in mind. After dinner we adjourned to the sitting room, where a large log fire was roaring in the grate, with a bottle of filthy red wine – the sort of plonk my mate Fritz and I wouldn't even have drunk when we were about fifteen – warming on the hearth. She dismissed the butler for the night, and insisted I go and sit next to her on the sofa. A real gruesome twosome!

She came straight to the point.

'I hear you've split up with your girlfriend. Are you looking for another?'

'Yes . . .'

'What sort of age?'

'I'm not bothered – any age will do!'

'Well . . . Do you know what we do on the farm here? We put the young boars in with the old sows, and the old sows teach the young boars how to do the business . . .'

I panicked. 'Is that the time? I must be going!' – and I was out of there as quickly as I could move.

Not long after that, she expressed her disappointment with me by taking her horses elsewhere. I assume the next trainer stayed a bit longer after dinner than I had . . .

Trainers are nothing without owners, and the vast majority of owners put up with a great amount of expense and disappointment with the minimum of fuss. But even the most generous-spirited trainer would have to concede that some owners would tax the patience of a saint.

One of my owners so drove me up the wall that I wrote her a letter:

Thank you for your two sides of A4 spelling out your complaints. I have the telephone number of a very good psychiatrist. Would you like to have it?

She replied:

If you go to him he can't be much good.

As in any working relationship, sometimes trainer and owner click, sometimes they don't – and if they don't, there's not too much that can be done about it.

The good owner is easily characterised: patient, long-suffering, realistic about the financial and emotional hazards of racehorse ownership, and – crucially – prompt in the payment of training bills.

The worst type of racehorse owner is the successful businessman who wants to own racehorses purely to publicise to a wider audience just how successful he is. He has no interest in the horse as such as long as it runs where he wants it to and when he wants it to – that is, where he can show off to the largest number of people. The horse is nothing more than an extension of his ego.

The problem is that the owner's plans very rarely suit what is right for the horse. I was very lucky in that I had very few owners like this, and those that I did have were not involved with Uplands for long.

Apart from prompt payment of bills, other gestures help oil the relationship between owner and yard. Nigel Dempster, diarist on the *Daily Mail* and a man who knows everyone who is anyone, was the only owner I've ever trained for who would write a thank-you letter to the lad who looked after his horses after each race. He was also very generous with the lads in a more tangible way, and understandably there was no shortage of volunteers to look after his horses.

Nigel was ridiculously enthusiastic about his horses, the two best of which during my time at Uplands were Switch, who won several races, and the very good chaser Aardwolf. But whatever the horse, we always gave plenty of attention to getting a decent lunch at the course before racing. These lunches were invariably pretty thirst-quenching occasions, and sometimes proved quite revealing about Nigel's skills as a social observer. On one occasion we ran Switch at Worcester, and I ordered roast beef – only to have to ask the waitress to remove the gravy she had poured all over it. A tiny matter, but six months later at Sandown Park, during another lunch with Nigel and his wife Camilla, my roast beef was served up ready smothered in gravy. 'Sorry, you'll have to take that back,' Nigel told the waitress, 'Charlie doesn't like gravy on his roast beef.' He forgets nothing about people.

Gravy-spotting apart, Nigel's great quality as an owner was his attitude towards victory and defeat. He loved winning – which owner doesn't? – but he always took defeat in his stride, and never displayed the sulkiness to which too many owners succumb in the immediate disappointment.

Andrew Lloyd Webber and his wife Madeleine were probably the highest-profile owners I trained for, and as with Nigel Dempster we had some good times together. An accomplished three-day-eventer, Madeleine is highly knowledgeable about horses and has been very much the driving force behind the couple's involvement with racing. Andrew himself had not had much to do with horses before he met Madeleine, but had the extremely useful asset of land in Berkshire ideally suited to rearing horses – free-draining limestone pasture. For a bit of fun, rather than as a serious business venture, Andrew bought Madeleine a few jumping horses in partnership with the impresario Robert Stigwood. Among their early runners was Dusty Miller, trained by Simon Sherwood to win several races including the County Hurdle at Cheltenham in 1992. Frank Rich, named after a Broadway theatre critic who had given Andrew considerable grief over the years, was a less successful buy: 'Never mind,' Andrew announced reassuringly, 'we can always eat him.'

The partnership with Robert Stigwood did not endure for very long, which was possibly a relief to Simon Marsh, who had taken on the role of managing the Lloyd Webbers' equine interests: he never seemed to relish his unchaperoned meetings with Stigwood. Simon (known to his friends as 'Pie', for reasons which have never been satisfactorily explained to me) cut a very different figure from most of the rest of the court of Lloyd Webber, whose smooth-talking financial and artistic advisers considered him something of a country bumpkin – the village idiot, even. When Simon and Madeleine, keen to develop the Watership Down Stud on the basis of buying the best, breeding to the best and hoping for the best, persuaded Andrew to part with $750,000 for the broodmare Silver Lane in the USA, the sneers of those advisers grew louder. They were coughing into their cornflakes again when IR£470,000 were splashed out to buy Darara, a chuck-out from the Aga Khan. And the condescending smiles were doubtless bouncing around the walls of the Really Useful Group's offices yet again when £500,000 was spent on Crystal Spray. But Andrew had total trust in the integrity of his manager and backed them all the way, and what happened next makes pretty good reading.

Silver Lane produced a yearling foal that sold for 200,000 guineas – not an overwhelming success in the light of her own purchase price, but the market was bound to be wary of a new operation until it had a well-established track record. Then the foal which Darara had been carrying when she'd been bought sold for 500,000 guineas, and a year later her next foal went for a similar price. The offspring that Crystal Spray had been carrying when bought sold as a yearling for 625,000 guineas. So two of the mares were well ahead of the game – and then Silver Lane, after having been rested for a year, produced a colt who proved the sale-topper at the Houghton Sale in Newmarket, going for 2.2 million guineas – a vast amount of money by anybody's standards, even Andrew Lloyd Webber's. That early investment was paying off.

No doubt there are those who find it difficult to fathom why a man with Andrew's financial resources should want to go to the trouble and expense of breeding these Thoroughbreds only to sell them. The answer is simple. To operate at the top end of the market there has to be a firm financial footing, otherwise only an oil well could sustain the effort. By selling the colts and keeping the fillies to race and eventually breed from, the operation should be able to sustain itself and grow.

Thankfully for me, the Lloyd Webbers decided that alongside their racing and breeding interests on the Flat they would continue to have a few jumpers – not that there was much financial sense in that! – and sale of David Bott's horses after his death in 1994 produced an ideal candidate for the Lloyd Webbers in the shape of Black Humour. He had won the Charisma Gold Cup at Kempton impressively in October 1993 and looked like having an outstanding chance in the Hennessy Gold Cup at Newbury the following month, and luckily for me the Lloyd Webbers bought him and agreed to leave him in the yard rather than move him to one of their existing trainers – even though Black Humour did not get the relationship off to a dream start in the Hennessy, where he could finish only third.

However hard we tried to help him, Black Humour never really mastered the art of self-preservation. As I've mentioned already, he fell in the Grand National, Cheltenham Gold Cup and Champion Hurdle, and broke Peter Scudamore's leg at Market Rasen while Scu was reigning champion jockey, ruining his chance of retaining his title. He also smashed up Jamie Osborne in the Martell Cup at Aintree in April 1996, by which time he had reached the venerable age of twelve and really should have known better.

Yet when he put his mind to it Black Humour could jump very well: he was brilliantly accurate and quick when he met a fence spot-on, and was very good when he met one long. But when he had to shorten his stride and fiddle an obstacle, it all went to pot. Physically he didn't seem able to sort himself out, and mentally he was as happy to lie down as to stand up. In truth, Black Humour was a little soft. If he'd been a human he would have been far too polite and sensitive to have reached the very top as an athlete. He undoubtedly had the ability to be anything and he did try, but he seemed to lack what a really good horse needs between the ears. If his sire had been Roy Keane instead of Buckskin, Black Humour would have been a champion.

One of the best things the Lloyd Webbers did for me was to introduce me to Anthony Pye-Jeary, whose company does the art-work for Andrew's musicals and who always seemed to know how to enjoy himself. When Lady Joseph died we persuaded Anthony to come into a partnership with the Lloyd Webbers to buy her good horse Padre Mio, who had never really taken to English steeplechase fences but was a very decent hurdler and just the sort of jumper with which we could campaign in Europe to pay his way. In spite of the fact that I felt that Lady Joseph's children disliked me, I felt I owed it to her to do the best I could for them, and that meant selling Padre Mio for as good a price as possible. So I advised them that before the horse went to the Ascot sales he should have a run on the Flat. The trouble was, if he ran well in a Flat race, his jockey might be so impressed that he'd tip off some other trainer to buy the horse at the sales, and Uplands would end up losing him.

I was in the office mulling over this problem and looking through the programme book of future races when Miriam walked in, and I had a brainwave: get Miriam to ride Padre Mio in the showpiece ladies' race at Ascot on Diamond Day in July, the day of the running of the prestigious King George VI and Queen Elizabeth Diamond Stakes. A good run from the horse on such a high-profile occasion would advertise his worth, yet by getting Miriam to ride him we would, as it were, be keeping it in the family. Problem solved – or rather, problem solved if I could cajole Miriam into taking the ride. She was an accomplished horsewoman and had ridden in the occasional race before, and though it took a fair while and all my powers of persuasion, she eventually agreed.

On the day, Miriam's biggest problem was getting Padre Mio down to the start without getting pissed off, a feat she managed by trotting the whole way – that is, the reverse way down Ascot's round mile. This delayed the start, but at least horse and jockey were there in one piece. In the race itself Padre Mio and his partner turned in an absolute blinder and finished seventh behind Cap Juluca, who was an extremely good horse – though our chances of buying the horse back at the sales might not have been improved had anyone noticed Miriam being unable to pull Padre Mio up after passing the post and still going very nicely when they arrived down at Swinley Bottom.

We duly formed the partnership to buy the horse and acquired him from Lady Joseph's estate for 20,000 guineas. Our first plan, a couple of weeks after the purchase, was to run him in France at Clairefontaine.

Neither Anthony, Andrew nor Madeleine could make the trip, but that didn't stop Brad, Pie, Miriam and myself lording it in the Normandy Hotel.

The best thing about the Normandy is the free use of communal bicycles – and since that is just about the only thing you get for free in the Normandy we thought we'd put the facility to good use and go racing by bike, in that way keeping our expense sheets clear for the onslaught they were sustaining in the bar. Unfortunately for Brad the weights are always very light in France so he had to spend most of our trips there losing weight in the bath, and our cycling plans were nearly thwarted by Miriam's insistence that girls can't go round on bikes with their skirts up around their ears. In the end she decided she'd have to wear jeans, and since she refused to wear jeans if we were wearing suits, we had to dress down. I'd never before known her to be too fussed about how I was dressed, but since the key to the whole adventure rather had hinged on her participation, we decided to humour her. We went in our shorts.

The race meetings at Clairefontaine have a very holiday atmosphere so it didn't occur to me that wearing shorts might be frowned upon – and in addition they'd be nice and cool on a very hot day. Brad in particular cut a strange figure, cycling along with his saddles and other gear strapped to the back of his bike, and I suspect that the racecourse authorities took exception to his cycling right into the weighing room, tossing a jovial 'Bonjour!' at the clerk of the scales as he went past, then parking his bike next to his peg in the changing room.

I had got used to the fact that the French idea of welcoming you to their racecourse was to ignore you totally, and after a career in which I have had winners at Auteuil, Clairefontaine, Enghien and Cagnes-sur-Mer, I cannot remember one instance of a representative of the track coming up to say well done or bad luck or hello or goodbye or – much more important – would you like a drink or a spot of lunch? Even so, my dim view of French racecourse hospitality had not prepared me for being refused access to the weighing-room area on account of the deeply offensive nature of my baggy khaki shorts. Eventually a deal was struck whereby they wouldn't let me in but they'd allow Miriam in instead, which caused a bit of confusion among the punters: 'Ah, Charlie Brooks – c'est une femme!'

We'd decided that at 5–1 with the pari-mutuel, Padre Mio was something of a good thing – or rather he was a good thing until Pie deposited bundles of Anthony's hard-earned dosh with a woman at the pari-mutuel window who had clearly never seen so much of the stuff in her life. Since there is only pool betting on French racecourses you cannot take a price – you are paid out at whatever the declared tote dividend is – and by the time Pie came away from the window, Padre Mio's price had shrunk to 6–4 on and smoke was coming out of the machine.

For my own part I'd been too nervous about the race to have a bet, but 'the Padre' duly hacked up – at which point the powers that be, still agitated about my shorts, did their best to keep me out of the winner's enclosure: some bloke who I think might have been president of the racecourse came up and said that as I'd just trained the winner he hoped I'd now be able to afford a proper pair of trousers.

I may not have made many French friends on that trip, but at least Padre Mio had won a decent prize without ruining his handicap mark back home, since there were no direct form lines with which to relate his French form to his British. As a consequence he seemed well in for a very valuable handicap hurdle at Listowel in County Kerry, and Anthony made sure he didn't miss that trip.

I had just come out of hospital after a serious knee operation (two artificial ligaments) and was feeling terrible – in so much pain that I could scarcely get from my bed to the bathroom. An infection had set in, which I was treating with a course of antibiotics, and on our first evening in Listowel I phoned Miriam at home.

'Have you taken your antibiotics?' she asked.

'Yeeeessss,' I replied in my best hen-pecked schoolboy voice. 'I've taken all three of them.'

'All three?' she queried. 'You've only been prescribed two sorts.'

It turned out that as well as the antibiotics I'd been dosing myself up with the dogs' worming pills, and on reflection I'd thought they tasted a bit funny.

We stayed at the Dunraven Arms in Adare, the best hotel in Ireland in which to have a good time. Thank God that two of our runners, 'the Padre' and Go Universal, both won, as in my condition I simply could not have faced depressed owners. Unfortunately our third, Nigel Dempster's chaser Aardwolf, ran like a hairy goat – but Nigel, as ever, took it all in his stride.

On this occasion Anthony did get an acceptable price about Padre Mio, and the winnings were well invested at the Dunraven Arms (who did not even mind that we drew an advanced version of our new board game

'And They're Off!' on one of their best linen tablecloths). Anthony's efforts in foreign parts on behalf of the Lloyd Webbers are well attested by the bill he sent them on his return:

INVOICE

To: the reimbursement of expenses incurred re: Padre Mio at Deauville on 10/11 August 1995 and Listowel 27/28 September 1995.

Tourettes-sur-Loup Bar du Sport sundries	265.50
Additional six cases of local Rose	360.00
Damage to rented accommodation	488.00
Damage to liver	incalculable
Resultant medical care	530.00
Milk Thistle tablets	120.00
Assorted Listowel bar expenses	940.00
Additional Guinness	306.00
Losses incurred re 'And They're Off!'	200.00
Chambermaid expenses	150.00
Alka Seltzer and throat lozenges	4.00
New wardrobe due to expanded girth	1740.00
General wear and tear	100.00
Personal counselling fees	250.00
Loss of earnings (approx.)	5.00
Loss of memory	forgotten
TOTAL	£5458.50

Andrew Lloyd Webber did not absent himself from all our racing trips, and the night before Black Humour made his single-handed attempt at destroying the Chair fence at Aintree in the 1994 Grand National, Francesca de Ferranti had us all to stay in Cheshire, just twenty minutes by helicopter from the racecourse. This suited Andrew very well, as there were plenty of churches nearby for him to go and visit, enabling him to indulge in one of his greatest hobbies. It also suited the rest of us very well, as it meant that we could get very drunk the night before the National and not have to be at the racecourse at the crack of dawn to witness the horses cantering and Jenny Pitman milking the whole thing.

'And They're Off!' was a racing board game which I'd had in my mind over a period of months, and halfway through the evening I showed Andrew the prototype. This really caught his imagination: I discovered to my surprise that he'd always had a hankering to develop a board game, and he reckoned that with a bit more effort this could be exactly what he was looking for. We settled on the name 'And They're Off!' to try to appeal to the US market, since that is what is always shouted by the commentator at the start of the Kentucky Derby, but the game did not prove the commercial success we were hoping for. It did have its fans, however: John Inverdale got me on to his Radio Five Live programme *Any Sporting Questions?* on the strength of it, and Alison Curbishley, one of our best runners, got quite animated when I told her I'd helped develop the game, as she claimed it was her all-time favourite. One critic even called it the best board game since *Monopoly*. Unfortunately for us, it turned out to be something of a cult taste.

Andrew Lloyd Webber may have less expert knowledge of horses than his wife, but he's never been shy of getting as much fun as he can from her interest in the sport – and he loves nothing better than winding people up. A few years ago the top lady jockey in France was 'Mademoiselle Madeleine', and the enthusiasm with which Andrew and I were cheering home this glamorous rider at Cagnes-sur-Mer left Andrew's own Madeleine distinctly unimpressed – to the extent that she became somewhat stroppy about it. Seeing the chance for a decent practical joke, Andrew phoned me soon after we'd returned from France and asked me to send his Madeleine a fax saying that I was not happy that Graham Bradley should ride her horse Garolo at Cheltenham, and since I believed that a French-bred horse should have a French rider, I'd booked Mademoiselle Madeleine for the ride. Andrew collected the fax from their machine and casually left it on the sofa for Madeleine to pick up, then hid at the end of the room so that he could see her reaction. Sure enough, she took the bait, and her reaction was very satisfactory.

Andrew proved a significant ally in my opposition to the building of the Newbury bypass in the mid-1990s – though my involvement in this was hugely overblown in the press. Some papers had me sitting in a tree next to Swampy, whereas the reality was that I was at that time in the middle of operations on my knee and tree-climbing was out of the question.

No one disputed that the traffic in Newbury was appalling and something needed to be done, but to put that road through such beautiful and scientifically significant countryside seemed to me no more than an act of vandalism, though my view was not shared by many others in the local community. Andrew Lloyd Webber and Paul

Cole backed me, but Nicky Henderson was so keenly of the opposite opinion that at lunch one day he refused to serve me any wine unless I rescinded my views! Either you pour me wine or I go home, I demanded, and luckily he backed down.

My most public display of my views was limping part of the way on a protest march along the proposed route, but by then the area was attracting some pretty unsavoury types, so perhaps it's just as well that I was in no position to chain myself to a tree or join Swampy and his pals.

And it's thanks to the Lloyd Webbers that I was able to give signal service to a grateful nation by saving Sir David Frost from drowning.

In the summer of 1996 Andrew and Madeleine took a boat in the Mediterranean, and a few of us – including myself and Miriam and Sir David Frost with his wife Carina – spent ten unbelievable days eating and drinking our way down the Italian coast and around Sicily. Anthony Pye-Jeary was in charge of fishing, Andrew himself in charge of egg racing, and 'Pie' Marsh had to organise the cross-dressing party. I'd managed to avoid the more arduous duties, so Carina Frost decided that I should take David out on a jet-ski – just quietly pottering up and down the beach, as David couldn't swim.

This was easier said than done, since going slowly on a jet-ski is rather like going slowly on a motor-bike: the slower you go, the easier it is to topple over. We set off well enough but then had to go round a boat which was moored near the beach, and as we slowed to make the turning we lost our balance. Into the water we went, well out of our depth, and although we were both wearing lifejackets I knew that we were in a bit of trouble. I had gone under on an out breath and found myself under the jet-ski – and under David. With no air in my lungs at all I knew I had to get back above water as quickly as possible. For a moment I thought I'd had it, then forced my way to the surface – and there was Frosty splashing about all over the place. I told him to put his arms round my neck, and once he'd gratefully done so I started to breaststroke back towards the shore. We were halfway there and going nicely when he spotted the boat we had been trying to circumnavigate, disengaged himself from me and struck out towards it.

I couldn't believe this – what a moment to decide he could swim after all! But I set off in pursuit of him, and helped him up into the boat. This was not easy – I'm sure he won't mind my saying that if he were a jockey he'd have difficulty doing light – but we managed it and he was saved.

The next day there was another expedition on the jet-ski, but I stayed on the boat with Andrew. I'd had enough excitement for a while.

Alex Ferguson, legendary manager of the all-conquering Manchester United, has been a hero of mine for years and, knowing of his keen interest in racing, I'd been dying to meet him. My chance finally came one year at Royal Ascot. It's fair to say that I'd had a pretty good lunch that day, and was so over-excited at being introduced to my football idol that I don't think I can have made too much sense. It's never easy to meet one of your all-time heroes, but it's much harder when you've had a skinful, and I was convinced that I made a terrible impression on the great man.

At the next year's Cheltenham Festival I was working for Radio Five, and to my great chagrin was stuck down in the paddock with John Inverdale while Clare Balding was interviewing Alex up in the stand. I was irritated that I'd missed the chance to correct the terrible impression I'd given at our first meeting, but that, it seemed, was that.

After we were off air I was wandering up to the Lloyd Webbers' box in search of Dutch courage before Double Symphony ran in the Cathcart, still cursing my luck that I hadn't got to speak to Alex. As I wandered along an empty corridor I looked up – and there, walking straight towards me, was the saviour of Manchester United. If it had been Raquel Welch with no clothes on my heart wouldn't have beaten any faster, but I couldn't just let him walk on without saying something to him. What, though? The anorak in me was longing to ask how Gary Pallister's back was, but would that be too boring an approach? This terrible dilemma of whether or not to make a real prat of myself was churning around in my mind as he came nearer and nearer, and as he came up to me I just smiled weakly and opened my mouth in the hope that something would come out.

And what happened next? Why, Alex Ferguson smiled at me and said: 'Hi, Charlie! How are you doing?'

It was one of the great moments of my life, right up there with Observe winning the Foxhunter Chase, Manchester United themselves landing the 1977 FA Cup, discovering that my reproductive system functioned normally after all (I'd had my doubts), and Ryan Giggs's goal against Arsenal in the 1999 FA Cup semi-final replay. Alex Ferguson saying 'hi!' to me . . .

Alex had been interested in racing for a while, and had

decided to increase his involvement by buying into a few horses. Racing would both provide a distraction from the extreme pressures of football management and give him an interest he could share with his wife Cathy, who manages to remain dispassionate about the goings-on at Old Trafford. I stayed at the Ferguson home after the European Cup game against Bayern Munich at Old Trafford in 1998, and when we returned from the ground Cathy had no idea what the score had been: she'd been watching UK Gold. 'You all look quite happy – the match went OK, did it?' was her reaction as we entered the house.

When Alex started looking to buy a racehorse or two, it naturally made sense for him to concentrate on the Flat, since that way his horses would be more likely to be running during the summer months when he had more time to watch them. He bought a couple of Flat horses to go into training with Jack Berry and with Ed Dunlop, and shortly afterwards Miriam bumped into him at the sales in Newmarket. She laid it on thick about what a fan of his I was and how disappointed I'd been that he didn't appear to want to own jumpers, and he agreed to buy a jumper for me to train. We put together a partnership to give us a little more financial fire-power, and in due course found a very nice horse, then with Arthur Moore in Ireland, named Yankee Lord. He was already owned by an existing client of mine, John Halliday, and John kept a share for himself.

Sadly, Yankee Lord was sick when he arrived at Uplands; but, faced with a period of inactivity by his new acqui-sition, Fergie immediately showed his great quality as an owner: like other footballing legends who have made their mark in racing – Francis Lee, Mick Quinn and the spectacularly successful Mick Channon – he understands about training athletes, and understands what can and can't happen when things go wrong. With Alex, there was never any of the 'Well, he must be OK by now' with which plenty of other owners nag their trainers. His attitude, bred from decades appreciating the nature of human athletes, was always: 'Don't rush him.'

So I didn't rush him. Yankee Lord seemed to be suffering from the same condition as many horses who come over to England from Ireland and are never quite right until they've spent a good spring or summer at grass (perhaps it's caused by the change of water), and after he had been at Uplands for a couple of months I roughed him off and turned him out into a field for the spring.

What really strikes me about Alex Ferguson is a steely quality which I have only ever seen in one other man: Fred Winter. Having been lucky enough to spend a good deal of time with both of them, I've been in a position to make that comparison, and it seems to be more than simply a toughness – though no one would deny that of either man. The quality is better characterised as a dogged determination, a refusal to accept less than a complete commitment from everyone involved in their operation, a ruthlessness that wouldn't hesitate at removing anyone who can't give everything. One November morning Graham Bradley and I went to watch Manchester United training. Alex was quite happy to let Brian Kidd (then his assistant) run the session under his careful eye, but he missed nothing. His steel showed through when he told us how the previous evening he'd gone to watch the youth team play: 'At half time I told them they could all pack their bags and leave if that was the best they could do.' He was not bullshitting: he meant it very seriously, and I could imagine Fred Winter having taken exactly the same line. To reach the very top as a football manager or racehorse trainer it's not enough simply to be competitive: you need that extra strength of backbone which all the greats have – and Alex has a backbone of reinforced steel.

I like to think that he and I got on so well because each of us found the other's world both fascinating and diverting. He loved coming to Uplands to see the horses train; I loved going to Manchester to watch the players prepare for a big match. Although owning racehorses has never struck me as a particularly effective way to relax, the contrast between Alex on the touchline during a game and Alex watching his horses on the racecourse suggests that it works a treat for him.

When I left Uplands I was very worried that Yankee Lord wouldn't work out, but Simon Sherwood did well with him in his first season in charge of the yard, and all being well he'll make a good three-mile chaser.

Most trainers – especially over jumps – will agree that the 'old-fashioned' sort of owner causes the fewest problems. They know that horses can need time and patience, and they don't put their trainers under pressure to run a horse before it is ready. Taking over from Fred Winter, I was blessed with several owners from the old school who stayed loyal to Uplands after Fred's retirement.

None was more straight in his dealings with me than Dick Whittle, who had had horses with Peter Cundell and had decided to find a new trainer. In order to bring this about he held a 'beauty parade' of potential handlers, and I think he loved visiting all the candidates and poking his nose into all the nooks and crannies of the yard. I eventually won the beauty contest, not because he preferred me to everyone else, but because he wanted to prove me wrong. He'd asked me over to cast an eye over his pride and joy, a great big potential chaser by Oats. The horse was led out of its box, and with his big, silly, proud smile spreading across his face Dick puffed himself up – there was a fair bit of him to puff – and asked me what I thought.

I had a good look at the horse and announced: 'He looks like a great big boat to me.' Then I discovered, to my horror, that this was the very horse he wanted to put into training. It was the worst possible comment to have made, though in my defence I have to say that at this stage of his life Dick did both himself and his horses rather well, with the result that the 'great big boat' had a massive tummy on him and bore little resemblance to an equine athlete. Dick was outraged by my observation – but then decided to send the horse to me to prove just how wrong I was. When he sent me the horse's passport he included a letter:

> I enclose the Oats passport. You will see that I have named him after the response I always got from Padge Berry, who is a born optimist. He certainly is a big boy and they are usually very good – or useless! Let us hope it is the former.

Even when race-fit that horse weighed around 720 kilos – the heaviest I've ever had – but he was Couldnt Be Better, who won the Hennessy Gold Cup in 1995.

Dick, who sadly died early in 1998, was a great man to train for and we had a wonderful relationship, but the euphoria of that Hennessy victory must have got to him a little, as a few days after the race he came into the office and told me where the horse should run next.

'Dick,' I told him, 'please forgive me for quoting Robert Sangster, but there's an expression about how when the passengers go up to the cockpit and start flying the plane, it's time to bail out. We're doing all right with me flying this plane, so why don't I carry on flying it and you go back into the cabin?' You could only make that sort of remark to an old-fashioned owner, and he laughed – Dick was a big enough man to take this impertinence – but knew that I was only half joking, not because we didn't discuss plans at length, but because I didn't want to be excluded from any discussions.

Dick always liked to have a plan, and towards the end of 1995, after Couldnt Be Better's victory in the Hennessy, I hatched what was by any standards a fairly unusual one. All his life Couldnt Be Better had been prone to 'bleeding' – the haemorrhaging of blood into the lungs when the horse is fully exerting himself. Couldnt Be Better was what I thought of as a genetic bleeder, meaning that he had his problem because of the way nature had designed him, rather than because he was or had been ill. Over previous years the problem seemed to get worse as the racing season went on, and we decided that if we were going to have any chance of the horse performing well in the Cheltenham Gold Cup in mid-March we had to create in Couldnt Be Better's body the illusion that March was the beginning of the season, not the end. To do this we decided to send him to a much warmer climate, and packed him off before Christmas with Padre Mio and Garolo to Cagnes-sur-Mer – where they were both running – and then on to Pisa. The theory was one that we had 'borrowed' from Vincent O'Brien, greatest of Irish trainers, who in the winter of 1967–8 had sent his great Classic hope Sir Ivor from his yard in County Tipperary to Pisa to benefit from the warmer climate. The experience certainly hadn't done Sir Ivor any harm – he won the Two Thousand Guineas, Derby and Washington International in 1968 – and I was hopeful that the warm and dry conditions could make all the difference to Couldnt Be Better.

I was half right. Every day I compared the temperature in Pisa with that in Lambourn by speaking on the phone to Tony McKeown – a wonderful stableman whom we sent out to look after the horse – and it was always ten degrees warmer there than in Berkshire. But the gallops and training facilities were very different from what Couldnt Be Better was used to, and the idea that it would be dry, and thus good for the horse's wind, couldn't have been further from the truth: it hardly stopped raining all the time Couldnt Be Better was in Pisa.

An additional factor in the success of this operation is that Tony managed to put up with being on his own in a strange country, whereas sometimes these operations fall down because people get homesick and bored. He coped with the dislocation brilliantly. He weighed the horse every day, and worked him as much as he could in order to get him down to close to his racing weight; then ten days before the Gold Cup we brought him back to Uplands. In the paddock at Cheltenham he looked quite magnificent, his coat a different class from any other runner's, and he rewarded us by running the best race of his life to finish third behind Imperial Call.

Couldnt Be Better ran in the Gold Cup without the benefit of a serious piece of work at Lambourn on his return, and in retrospect it might have been better to have brought him back twelve days before the race and given him a major piece of work on Lasix – the anti-bleeding drug which has to have disappeared from a horse's system before it runs. (The pros and cons of Lasix are discussed elsewhere in this book.) None the less, Couldnt Be Better's performance at Cheltenham bore ample testimony to the sense of attempting the unusual – and to Dick Whittle's agreeing to what to many other owners would have seemed like a strange suggestion from their trainer.

Another of the great men of the Turf for whom I had the privilege of training was Bill Tulloch. Bill loved every aspect of racing, and took especially seriously his duties as a steward at Chepstow – so seriously that he always struck me as a great argument in favour of the present system of having three unpaid local stewards, with a professional stipendiary steward (popularly known as a 'stipe') to advise them about the finer points of the Rules of Racing, rather than – as is the clamour from some quarters – professional stewards. I have never thought that the sport would be improved by full-time professional stewards. First and foremost, unpaid local stewards turn up for their stint without any axe to grind, and they have an outstanding record of being far removed from any corruption or favour. Of course they make mistakes and are sometimes inconsistent, but so are nurses, doctors, jockeys, airline pilots, gynaecologists, lawyers, roadsweepers and racehorse trainers (that should just about cover it). But the local stewards are honest, well trained and more suitable than full-time pros who might fall out with a jockey or trainer and pursue him from Ayr to Brighton. At least with local stewards that is not going to happen.

Bill Tulloch loved stewarding, but most of all he loved owning horses, and his passion was rewarded with many top-class performers. The best horse I trained for him and his wife Georgina was My Young Man, and he did very well with Stan Mellor through horses like Lean Ar Aghaidh, who was third in the Grand National and won the Whitbread, and top-class hurdlers Meladon and Pollardstown. They also did very well on the Flat with Wind In Her Hair, runner-up to Balanchine in the 1994 Oaks when trained by John Hills, and with Mahogany and Creag-An-Sgor, both trained by Bill's cousin Charlie Nelson (son of Peter Nelson, who won the Derby in 1974 with Snow Knight). Charlie paid 20,000 guineas for each of these at the yearling sales, which was a hefty sum when the usual price for a 'fun' horse on the Flat was around 7,000 guineas, but was soon rewarded when in 1983 Creag-An-Sgor won the Middle Park Stakes, one of the season's top two-year-old races; and on one glorious weekend in April 1984 this pair won both the Newbury Classic trials on consecutive days.

On the Friday, Mahogany (whom the Tullochs owned in partnership with Marcel Klein and Charlie) won the Fred Darling Stakes to set her up for a crack at the One Thousand Guineas, and on the Saturday morning the connections met in The Swan at Great Shefford en route to the races.

'Charlie!', exclaimed Georgina, flinging her arms around her trainer, 'we're so excited about yesterday – it really doesn't matter what happens with Creag-An-Sgor today.'

'Of course it does,' Bill corrected her. 'I've got him in a double with Mahogany.'

Creag-An-Sgor duly landed Bill his double when gamely winning the Greenham Stakes; but had he lost Bill, a brave punter who loved nothing better than getting one over on the bookmakers, would have taken it in his stride: he knew that it was in the nature of the game that you had to accept the losers with the winners.

But he was also thrilled to own a really good horse, and before the One Thousand Guineas turned down an offer of £2 million for Mahogany. As far as Bill was concerned, once he had a good horse he was going to keep it, though passing up £2 million did not come easily. When in the paddock before the Guineas he was asked by Georgina whether he liked her hat, he replied: 'Yes – it's probably cost me £2 million.'

Sadly, Mahogany flopped in the One Thousand Guineas and never recaptured her best form. She was sold as a broodmare.

Unfortunately I was responsible for denting what would surely have been the finest hour of Bill's punting career. He was going to France for a Bank Holiday weekend in May 1989 and decided to phone round some of his trainer friends for a few good things to bet on before he went. Charlie Nelson, John Hills and myself each gave him a couple of ours we hoped would win, and another friend had a runner that he fancied strongly. Seven horses, and Bill backed them in every imaginable combination.

By the Saturday night the first six had all won –

including one of my contributions, Arden at Haydock Park – and the only remaining runner was my horse Run On Stirling in an amateur riders' novice hurdle at Fakenham on the Bank Holiday Monday. I'd thought she would be good value as I knew she had potential, even though she'd shown very little form (tailed off on her only run), but on the Saturday morning she had worked very badly, and when Bill phoned from France on the Saturday evening I had to break the news that my confidence was rapidly ebbing away.

This was not at all what he wanted to hear. Bill asked if she really had to run on the Monday; I had to tell him that the owners were very keen for her to run and I couldn't withdraw her to protect Bill's bet. The only solution I could think of was that he himself buy Run On Stirling pretty sharpish and withdraw the horse from her Fakenham engagement. I'm sure that if Bill had been in England that's exactly what he would have done, but he decided to leave things as they were and just hope for the best.

Run On Stirling should have been a 33–1 shot in the Fakenham race, but whichever bookmaker was bearing the liability of Bill Tulloch's bet had sent a man up to smash into the starting price, and to the astonishment of her owners she went off odds-on favourite. With John Durkan riding, she was beaten nine lengths – the best run of her life, but not good enough to put the icing on Bill's bet.

To rub salt into the wound, I had two winners at Fakenham that day, Hazy Sunset at 7–1 and Lattin General at 5–1. Why the hell hadn't I told Bill to back one of them?

A couple of years later I was admiring Bill's new tennis court at their home in Scotland – and discovered that it had been built from the proceeds of the six out of seven. But I thought I could detect an 'if only' look in Bill's eye as he informed me of this . . .

Five years later I went at least some way towards redressing the balance. When Charlie Nelson stopped training, Bill sent me Fieldridge, who was a good horse on his day but a bit of an old shit: he didn't much fancy the hurly-burly of a hurdle race, but he still had an engine and there were races to be won with him.

On Derby Day 1993 Fieldridge ran in the Silver Seal Handicap at Epsom, two races after the Derby itself, and was ridden by Pat Eddery, still smarting from defeat in the big race on odds-on favourite Tenby. When Pat arrived in the paddock he looked very pissed off indeed, which delighted Bill, on the basis that 'I like it when they're angry – they go out in a fighting mood.' How right he was! Pat, with a little help from his stick, lifted Fieldridge over the line to win by a short head. The horse himself was not that impressed by the experience and declined to win for another year, even conspiring to get beaten at Exeter and thus be our only loser from eleven runners at the start of the next season. But Fieldridge's place in Bill Tulloch's affections was secure after a great rescue act in June 1994.

Royal Ascot that year had been a disaster for Bill: he backed twenty losers in a row. On the Friday that the Royal meeting closed, Fieldridge was running in the evening at Goodwood, and although I had not been racing at Ascot I picked Bill up from there and drove him down to Sussex. Having witnessed his catastrophic punting at Ascot and fearing more of the same that evening, none of Bill's family would come down with us, and nor would Charlie Nelson: they all skulked back to Charlie's for dinner.

On that trip down to Sussex, Bill was at the lowest ebb I'd ever seen him, but he was a true warrior as far as his betting was concerned, and he bombarded me with questions. Is the horse's back OK? Is his mind OK? Is the trip right? Is the going right? I gave him positive answers to all his enquiries, and on arriving at the course he went straight to the bookies and bet his maximum. For my own part I was far too nervous to back Fieldridge, but this time there was a happy ending, as the old dog decided to put his best foot forward for a change, and under the hefty weight of 9st 13lb – Ray Cochrane and a lot of lead – he won easily at 11–2. We gave the faint-hearts some stick when we arrived back at Charlie Nelson's!

There's so often an element of Sod's Law with owners: the nicest ones don't get the success their devotion to the sport merits, and the nastiest bastards have a level of winners which they just don't deserve. We had an owner at Uplands called Mary Talbot, who was a wonderful lady to train for but simply couldn't get a horse worthy of her enthusiasm. One of her horses in Fred's day was San Ovac, an idle devil who won a few races but never produced the kind of form of which we knew he was capable. One day at Towcester he pulled up, and when I heard this on getting back to the stables after having been racing elsewhere, I rang Miss Talbot to commiserate. 'Don't worry,' she said. 'He had a lovely wash-down.' She'd been happy just to see her horse being washed down after the race! I'd have done anything to have found a good horse for her, but it just wasn't to be. One year I bought two horses from Tom Costello in Ireland and offered her first choice. The one she chose proved useless. The other turned out to be Hoh Warrior, who became a high-class horse. Such was her luck, but she never groused for a second.

If only they were all like that – but of course they're not. For every uncomplaining Miss Talbot, there are half a dozen owners who won't pay their bills on time, complain about those bills when they finally get round to paying them, and blame everyone in sight when their horse fails to win. Mind you, when they get a bill like this one, you can see their point:

1 May to 31 May: training fees at £35 per day	£1085.00
to routine vet	£10.00
to blacksmith	£65.00
to flu vaccination	£25.75
to blood test twice	£70.00
to scope and trachea wash twice	£109.26
to rasp teeth	£19.45
to gallop fees for May	£85.00
to insurance certificate	£27.70
9 May: transport to Folkestone	£290.00
to lads' expenses	£36.00
24 May: transport to Ayr (no shares available)	£663.00
to lads' expenses (overnight)	£86.20
to trainer's flight to Ayr	£119.00
to treatment from chiropractor	£35.00
to vets to scan tendon	£79.28

to jockey's retainer for 1999 season	£500.00
Total	£3305.64
VAT	£578.49
Invoice total	£3884.13

The Owner From Hell is incapable of seeing things in perspective, and usually suffers from simple ignorance – both about horses and about what he is letting himself in for when embarking upon ownership. When talking to a prospective first-time owner, I always used to do my best to put them off, pointing out that there was little realistic chance of making money at the game, reminding them of the old racing adage that the only way to make a small fortune from owning racehorses is to start with a large one, and alerting them to all the pitfalls and disappointments that lay along the way. There's little likelihood of a tangible asset at the end of the day, so you'd better be prepared to enjoy the venture even if you're completely unsuccessful.

One owner who clearly did not enjoy having horses with me was Geoff Meadows. He had a horse called Fort Noel with Josh Gifford, and when I had to phone Josh to let him know that Meadows had asked me to take this horse on, he didn't seem too surprised – nor, I was uneasy to discover, too disappointed. Josh had thought a great deal of Fort Noel and was glad he was going to a good home (a typical attitude from Josh, who exemplifies everything that is good about National Hunt racing), but was clearly not despondent about losing Mr Meadows.

I soon found out why. Fort Noel was sidelined by leg

trouble and Meadows asked me to find him a replacement, which I did in France in the form of Gold Cap, an inexpensive purchase who looked ideal for the four-miler at the Cheltenham Festival. Having come over to Uplands, Gold Cap acclimatised well and was ready to run in a small race to give him his first experience of English fences, an ideal start on the way to Cheltenham. However, a small race was not what Geoff Meadows had in mind, and he insisted that we run Gold Cap in the Fairlawne Chase at Windsor, usually a good-class event for horses tuning up for Cheltenham. I pointed out that I already had Espy aimed at the Fairlawne, and there was no way – so far as we could tell – that Gold Cap was yet in his class. Also, there was the risk that if Gold Cap finished close to Espy he would bugger up his handicap mark for the future. Whichever way you looked at it, Gold Cap should not run in the Fairlawne. Better go for an easier option.

But Meadows would have none of this and insisted on running the horse – and furthermore insisted that he be ridden by Richard Rowe, who I liked and admired as a jockey but who hadn't previously ridden for me.

In the paddock at Windsor I told Richard that Gold Cap would never beat Espy unless something went wrong with the other horse, and that he was to give him an enjoyable introduction to English racing and not hit him with the whip.

I took up my position on the stands as the runners were cantering to the start, and Meadows came and stood next to me.

'I've put £500 on Gold Cap for you,' he said, which was the only time in my training career that any owner put anything on for me – and a very unwelcome gift it was, since I thought Gold Cap could not win.

At that moment Espy dug his toes in and declined to go further. Never mind that £500 bet – this was no time for Espy to mess about, and I ran off the stand and sprinted across to lead him down. He got there safely, jumped off OK and duly beat Gold Cap without much fuss – though Geoff Meadows had obviously given Richard Rowe instructions which did not quite accord with mine, as he did hit the horse two or three times. Meadows had obviously decided that he knew best and had had a right punt on his horse, which would have paid off had Espy not started the race. He didn't look too pleased with me afterwards.

Gold Cap duly ran in the four-miler at the Cheltenham Festival and, ridden by Marcus Armytage, looked all over the winner coming down the hill for the last time, only to fall at the third last. It was a very hot day, and after the race Gold Cap collapsed: I thought he was about to breathe his last, but he was revived with oxygen and eventually got up to make the return trip, exhausted, to Uplands. I felt that the horse needed time to recover from such an experience, but to my amazement Geoff Meadows phoned to tell me he wanted to run the horse in a three-mile hurdle at Liverpool just a couple of weeks after Cheltenham. This was plain crazy. The horse desperately needed a rest after the Festival, and in any case to run an out-and-out stayer – as Gold Cap had proved himself to be – around the tight hurdle track at Liverpool was ridiculous.

I stood my ground and told him I was adamant that the horse should not run at Liverpool – and sure enough, one morning he rang me and said he was moving his horses from Uplands to Philip Hobbs. (I'm ashamed to recall that when Philip rang me to say he'd been asked to take the horses I was pretty cool with him, as I was next time I saw him. This was incredibly childish of me: you'd have thought I might have learned better behaviour from Josh Gifford.) When I suggested to Mr Meadows that I'd done a good job for him he didn't disagree, but he'd made his decision, and that was that. I was very pissed off to lose the horses, but not unhappy to see the back of their owner.

The worst characteristic of The Owner From Hell is that he's so busy trying to tell you how to do your job that he doesn't listen when you try to communicate with him about his horse.

Communication: you never get very far into any management manual without coming across that word, and a constant gripe of owners is that their trainers fail to communicate with them. Unlike some trainers who discourage their owners from constantly pestering them for information about each horse, I never had much problem with the regular callers, since if you speak with owners frequently you cannot be accused of failing to communicate. The problem comes with the reaction to what you're trying to communicate. I always used to enjoy talking with Nigel Dempster, for example, as he'd take the rough with the smooth and never got annoyed if the news about his horse was discouraging, or not what he wanted to hear, or downright bad. The difficult owner is the one you have to force yourself to ring – and therefore whom you avoid ringing – as you know that he's going to get irascible if you have bad news. This does not necessarily relate to that person's knowledge of horses – some owners who know nothing about horses take everything in their stride, some who know a great deal can be awful – but it does relate to their general attitude.

Since I was choosy about which owners I enjoyed communicating with, I was not proof against accusations of neglect, even if like most trainers I would always be putting the interests of the horse first. In my last season at Uplands I was due to run one of the best horses in the yard at Cheltenham. Then a routine trachea wash revealed that all was not well with the horse, and it would clearly have been harmful to run him. I promptly informed the owners:

> I did a routine trachea wash on your horse yesterday after work. The results, which I got to see this morning, quite clearly show he has a bacterial infection in his lungs. We would never have known without the test. He is flying at home.
>
> If we ran him on Sunday he would be hugely disappointing and the race would damage him. With a ten-day course of the right antibiotic it should clear up very quickly. I have enclosed the tests I did yesterday to give you an idea of what looks right and wrong. The N is short for neutrophils – white blood cells that are produced in the early stage of infection.

Despite what you might imagine would be a fairly persuasive point about a race actually doing the horse damage, the complaints duly arrived: I've altered my schedule to be at Cheltenham, etc., etc.

In a fax to Uplands, one of the owners did not hold back:

With the usual comment that 'owners know nothing' I would make the following observations:

(a) I am not convinced by this 'tracheal wash' analysis. I have run a horse with much worse N,M,L,B,E,E,P % than this, and it won by eight lengths on the Flat and was not sick afterwards. He was 'flying at home' and flew at the racecourse.

(b) If you ask vets to find problems, they will.

(c) You can't win if you don't run.

(d) I'm in racing to have fun. If I want to be beguiled and bewitched with medical matters, I can watch *Casualty*, *ER*, *Animal Hospital*, etc.

(e) All our other trainers call us regularly to let us know what's happening. Getting news from Uplands would require the KGB, FBI and MI5 to collaborate and help us. We are not monsters, just owners who shell out lots of 'dosh' in the hope of occasionally having some fun. I assure you we are not having a lot of fun at the moment.

Oh well: you can't please all the people all the time.

Worse than owners themselves are owners' friends. Owners' friends are lethal. To hear the owner talk, all his friends have as much knowledge of training racehorses as Vincent O'Brien, and as much knowledge of race-riding as Richard Dunwoody. They are blessed with the gift of hindsight, and are never more lethal than when telling the owner to tell the trainer just what the jockey did wrong.

A few seasons ago Brad was riding one of mine in a

steeplechase at Stratford. At each fence down the back straight he was asking the horse for a long one, and each time the horse responded. But it is one thing to ask a horse on the bridle to go long at a fence halfway through the race, quite another to try to find a long one at the last fence when the horse is tired and more likely to fall than to come up for his jockey. Coming to the last Brad sat still to make sure he got over it in one piece, and after a driving finish was narrowly beaten.

Cue owners' friends. 'Did you see that?' they raged: 'Bradley deliberately pulled that horse! He threw the race away! Call in the Jockey Club! Blah blah blah . . .'

It never ceases to amaze me how badly otherwise perfectly reasonable adults can behave when things don't go right on the racecourse. I've always been very competitive myself and I don't enjoy losing one little bit, but the petulance of some racehorse owners in defeat would shame the most wayward inhabitants of a kindergarten. The worst instance I witnessed during my training career was that of an owner and his wife who, when their horse fell during the race, left the stand without saying a word and, without pausing to find out about the well-being of horse or jockey, sulked their way straight to the car park, and were off. People like that shouldn't be allowed around horses.

Trainers, however, learn to co-exist with such people. Worst of all owners is not the whinger or the know-all but the bad payer.

Owners are usually billed monthly in arrears, on a particular basis according to the practice of that yard. Some trainers stipulate a basic weekly fee and charge extra for such items as medical matters (blood tests, trachea washes, etc.), farriery and transport to the races. Others average out items such as transport and charge a fixed fee for each trip to the races, whether it be from Lambourn to Newbury or to Kelso.

But however a bill is computed, it has to be paid, and chasing non-paying owners is a constant pain in the neck, particularly for the small trainer with only a few horses in his yard. A trainer operating on the scale of Henry Cecil or Michael Stoute, with hundreds of horses, can afford to take a robust view of non-paying owners, since that scale of operation can live with losing a horse or two if the final sanction of removing those horses from the yard is reached. But if the yard has a dozen horses, losing a couple would be a catastrophe, and trainers in that position bend over backwards to accommodate their tardy payers – and are duly taken advantage of in the process.

Few trainers are much good at credit control – they're far more concerned about how their horses worked second lot – and it's been easy for owners to prey on that weakness. If the Jockey Club were so minded they could help trainers immensely by taking a stricter line on owners behind with payment, but they tend to think that it's not a Jockey Club problem: trainers are running their own businesses, and they should stop moaning and get on with it. Admittedly there is a committee to which you can report bad payers, but in practice the system is unsatisfactory.

Over the years, the attitude of some members of the Jockey Club to trainers at times harks back to when jockeys were paid servants and trainers were paid grooms, and by and large there is little evidence to suggest that the Jockey Club as a body has ever shown much interest in being supportive of trainers. It should not be forgotten that individual members of the Jockey Club have had a considerable number of horses in training over the years – collectively more than any other group of people – and so have individually supported their own trainers financially through their patronage. But that is different from how the Jockey Club as an organisation has positioned itself, and the trainers themselves must bear some of the blame for the current situation, since they have allowed their representative body, the National Federation of Trainers, to exist without having enough clout. This is not the fault of the people who run the NTF or who serve on its council, and sadly it is an inescapable fact that it is impossible to get trainers to speak with one voice. Hence the present secretary of the NTF, Grant Harris, has to make representations in the full knowledge that he does not have a mandate from the entire profession. What small trainers want will clash with what big trainers want – and some of the biggest names are not even members.

The old wisdom was that a gentleman always paid his butcher, his tailor and his racehorse trainer promptly, in which case there are few gentlemen left. This was particularly noticeable when the recession of the late 1980s started to bite. Owners who you knew would cough up eventually took to defaulting completely, and people whose horses had been removed from the yard – amicably, you thought – chose not to pay the last couple of months' charges. When Andrew Cohen took over Uplands the chance to leave to his company all that nonsense of chasing money, which was so frustrating and dispiriting, was a real godsend. We may have lost a couple of owners who were affronted by the idea of settling on time, but that was a small price to pay for the huge increase in efficiency – and in the time saved to get on with my real job of training the horses.

One Uplands owner, having studied the farriery charge and not appreciating that his horse had had two sets of front shoes that month plus one set of hind shoes, was reduced to sarcasm: 'I didn't realise my horse had six feet.'

7

IN THE SADDLE

ALWAYS REMEMBER THE SMALL PRINT.

I didn't, and in my rush to get my riding boots and breeches on again, to feel the wind in my face, the thunder of the hooves and the sheer exhilaration of race-riding, that small print slipped my mind.

It had seemed such a great idea when the notion of resuming my less-than-glittering career in the saddle was first put to me. The Injured Jockeys Fund was staging a charity day at Wincanton in October 1998, about six months after my break with Andrew Cohen, and the epilogue to an afternoon of serious jump racing was a celebrity race over one and a quarter miles on the Flat.

In terms of celebrity I may not have been ranked with some of the best-known riders in the race. Jane Holderness-Roddam, a household name in dressage circles, was in the line-up, as was top show jumper Nick Skelton, and there were three generations of

Scudamores: sixteen-year-old Thomas, a budding point-to-point rider; his father Peter, then the winning-most jockey in National Hunt history (and, of course, the rider of countless winners from Uplands); and Peter's father Michael, a great jump jockey of the old school who had won the 1959 Grand National on Oxo.

I was determined to treat the venture seriously, but kept forgetting that small print: 'Jockeys to weigh out at twelve stone.' Now, twelve stone may sound plenty heavy enough, but those who share my enjoyment in putting away ten pints of bitter of an evening will understand my predicament. It's all very well trying to put yourself into a routine of famine, but what do you do when you get those phone calls?

'Come and have lunch at the World Matchplay Final at Wentworth. Ian's coming.' Ian is Ian Wooldridge, doyen of sports columnists on the *Daily Mail* and not a man who treats lunch with levity. Only a fool would turn down lunch with Ian. You don't actually get to eat much but you learn a great deal and talk to a lot of wine waiters, and you do find yourself in interesting company. Good fortune pitched me in with Angus Loughran – 'Statto' from television's *Fantasy Football*, BBC betting guru and a devoted punter – who had gone so long in a spread bet on Mark O'Meara that he was happy to let me have some of it. O'Meara duly obliged, and we all went home wiser, richer and happier. But my weight problem, like my girth, had expanded rather than contracted . . .

Three days later disaster struck again in the shape of another call. Charles Benson, international playboy and friend of the rich just as long as they stay rich, was having a party at the Ritz Club Casino: did I want to go? Oh, all right then, but I promised myself I'd only have the soup – surely no harm in that – and maybe just a couple of glasses of red wine (so long as it's Burgundy: less fattening than some others). But the glamour of the occasion was simply too much for a wide-eyed innocent, and especially too much for my diet. Nigel Havers nodded to me. So did Jackie Stewart. Bryan Ferry's wife Lucy told me what great friends she is with my sister and brother. Every glamorous Flat trainer in the land was there, and each of them told me how much more relaxed and happier I was looking now that I was no longer training. Nigel Dempster berated me for no longer troubling myself with his horses. All this glittering company was such a distraction that yet again the wasting routine slipped my mind as I tucked into a delicious chocolate pudding and a vast slab of cheese. By then the evening at the Ritz was coming to an end, but the damage had been done – and then Paul Cole decided that a visit to Tramp night-club was called for.

You can't beat dancing for losing weight. Unfortunately you can't beat the chips they serve in Tramp for putting it back on, and at three in the morning Miriam caught me tucking into a large plateful. Her disapproval of this spectacle was not down simply to her concern for my well-being. As owner of Mr President, my mount in the Wincanton race, she did not want to see her jockey putting up several stone overweight. But by then no amount of riding out or half-hearted efforts at trying to get fit would make much of an impression.

I enjoyed a devoted following as a jockey. Devoted, but rather exclusive. It consisted of (1) my mother, and (2) Steve Taylor, the Lambourn-based racing journalist responsible for the scurrilous but revealing 'Blowing Stone' column in the *Sporting Life Weekender*. His piece before the Wincanton race nailed his emotional colours firmly to the mast:

> I could not be more thrilled if Sir S. Matthews or T. Finney were pacing down the wings at Wembley or Mr R. Marciano were knocking them over in Madison Square Garden . . . But you would be wrong to assume my glee was at the return of L. K. Piggott or Desert Orchid. No, my joy unbounded is at the return to the saddle of C. P. E. Brooks . . . In the eighties he and the one-eyed no-brakes Fionnadoir (horse) had fence builders crying for mercy as they smashed their way around the racecourses of our green and pleasant land.

Have you ever had the feeling that someone might be taking the piss?

At last the big day came, and despite those little slip-ups during the final days of preparation I had never felt so well in my life as when I arrived at the racecourse. I had trained myself to a peak, had not had a drink for two and a half days, and in order to avoid ruining everything at the last minute, sat through lunch in the Injured Jockeys Fund's marquee at the racecourse without eating a morsel. My host at the lunch suggested that a glass of wine might serve as a calming influence and I was too polite to disagree – so I had four glasses of wine, plus a couple of scotches to act as a last-minute diuretic.

It was time to get changed.

The gaunt figure beside me in the changing room

Uplands, 1995. (*Trevor Jones*)

'Stopper' Francome leaving the Ascot paddock on Padre Mio, July 1995, being led up
one of the best travelling head lads of his generation, Chuck Norris. (*David Hastings*)

Two of the great stalwarts of my time at Uplands: (*above*) Couldnt Be Better (Dean Gallagher) flying the last before winning the 1995 Hennessy, and (*below*) Suny Bay (Jamie Osborne) in pursuit of winner Lord Gyllene in the 1997 Grand National. (Both *Gerry Cranham*)

With Sir Alex Ferguson on the Lambourn gallops – a great opportunity to pick his brains.

Party time at the 1998 World Cup in France with Kenny Dalglish (*above*) ... Gavin Hastings (*right*) ... Ally McCoist (*below*). It's good to see I remembered to pack my dressing gown.

Contemplating lunch with Lady Joseph.

With the Lloyd Webbers before the Larlawne Chase at Windsor ... trying to look nervous. (*Gerry Cranham*)

(*Above*) At Lambourn with Black Humour's companion Ernest. (*Daniel Abraham*)
(*Below*) Amazingly, Jamie Osborne and Black Humour both survived this dramatic parting of the ways at Liverpool. Black Humour never really got the hang of it. (*Kenneth Bright*)

With Graham Bradley after Couldnt Be Better's victory in the Thyestes Chase at Gowran Park, January 1997. (*Healy Racing Photographers*)

Receiving a bottle of the sponsor's product from Sir Peter O'Sullevan after his final race commentary, Suny Bay's victory in the Hennessy Cognac Gold Cup at Newbury, November 1997. (*Bernard Parkin*)

Hennessy

COGNA

NEWBURY RACECOURSE

It's not difficult to guess who sleeps in the middle of the bed ... (*Trevor Jones*)

looked awfully familiar, awfully like Lester Piggott. Surely I hadn't had *that* much to drink? But it was indeed Lester, at Wincanton to parade on Desert Orchid. On the other side of me was Graham Bradley. Between Lester and Brad – at last, a taste of the big time. I had arrived.

Scu was sitting opposite me, talking to no one – not even his son or father. He may have been retired for over five years, but the single-mindedness which made him champion jockey seven times was still very much part of his make-up. Even for this charity race, Scu had to be completely focused.

My own focusing was not helped by trainer Gay Kelleway, first lady jockey to ride a winner at Royal Ascot, coming into the changing room and telling the valet that she needed a bigger stick . . .

Weighing myself on the 'trying scales' – the set of changing-room scales which jockeys use to test that they're at the right weight before the formal weighing out – caused great merriment among those who witnessed the needle soaring towards the maximum mark, and I knew that drastic measures were called for.

First, slip into a pair of 'cheating boots' which weigh one ounce each: they'd be extremely uncomfortable to ride the race in, but they help the battle with the scales and are surreptitiously swapped for a more substantial pair after you've weighed out. Then distract the clerk of the scales – the racecourse official responsible for monitoring the weighing out of every jockey – and get a colleague to put his toe under the scales as I quickly sit on the seat.

'Thank you, Mr Brooks – twelve stone one pound.'

Just one pound overweight! I bolted before anyone

asked for a second look, and passed my saddle over to the trainer.

Problem number one may have been successfully overcome, but there was still the matter of the horse himself.

Mr President, a great big horse trained by Vic Soane, was in truculent mood when I first set eyes on him in the paddock, rearing up and generally misbehaving. He refused to stay in line on the way out to the course and did not do my confidence a whole lot of good by insisting on taking his own route down to the start, but at least we got there in one piece, and there were no other mishaps until the starter called us into line. This was it – my first ride in public since 1988, and my chance to show the world that the magic was still there.

Mr President made a rather individual response to the starter's instruction to line up: he jumped violently to the left and embedded himself in a nearby hedge, refusing to budge. I implored the other jockeys to help by coming over and giving Mr President a lead out of the hedge, but with the exception of Michael Scudamore they were too hell-bent on getting a good start themselves and refused to give up their positions in order to help out a comrade in distress.

Just as I was about to despair, of my horse as well as most of my fellow riders, Mr President took it into his head to leap out of the hedge and canter towards the start. This was my chance, and it probably wouldn't be repeated.

'Let them go!' I yelled at the starter, and to his credit he did as I suggested – with the result that as Mr President came in at full pelt the tape whizzed past his nose. He needed no further excuse. He dived to the left. I went straight on, over his head – and he managed to tread all over me before galloping off after the other horses, now well on their way and disappearing over the horizon.

After all my relentless training, all the wasting and self-denial, I had got no further than the starting line.

As sixty-six-year-old Michael Scudamore – the only gentleman in the race – rode Barneys Bell to a convincing victory (Michael's first winner for thirty-two years), I trudged back to the stands, where I was greeted by a very sporting owner Simon Tindall, who at the pre-race auction had paid £350 for Mr President in the sweep.

'What a pity,' said Simon, 'you were going so well.'

The Brooks riding career which ended so ignominiously in that hedge had commenced, somewhat tentatively, in point-to-points when I was sixteen.

My ambitions in the saddle were initially fuelled by the prospect of the succession of girls that would swoon in my direction as I coolly wandered around the beer tents at point-to-point meetings still in my riding clothes. But this ploy was singularly unsuccessful, because by the time I had got out of the ambulance, most of them had gone home.

Nor could I attract girls with the sweet scent of success, since I never won a point-to-point. I did, however, get plenty of practice at hitting the deck.

My mother and I had acquired a horse called Young American, who had the annoying knack of getting rid of me without himself appearing to have made a mistake. (The Prince of Wales was at that time having a similar problem with his horse Good Prospect, and I had a great deal of sympathy for him.) So I never seemed to get very far in a race, and consequently became extremely tired if by some chance I survived until the later stages. A stranger at a party in London with whom I was discussing this problem gave me a pill and recommended I take it half an hour before the race: 'You won't get tired then, I assure you!' Before my next point-to-point ride I did as he advised, and when the time came to get legged up in the paddock was running around like a headless chicken: they did well to catch me. What the helpful stranger had not told me was that this pill, as well as prolonging my stamina, was likely to give a large boost to my confidence – with the result that at the first open ditch I asked my conveyance to stand off about three strides early, and we took a crashing fall. For a few minutes I was stunned, which gave the St John Ambulance men the chance to get me on to a stretcher and into the back of the ambulance. But that pill was still working its magic with my system, and by the time the ambulance men got to the medical tent their patient had long gone.

Chris Sweeting, a neighbour and a man who had been around the point-to-point game long enough to know what's what, was enlisted to improve my skills, and he must have appreciated the magnitude of his task at our first schooling session. Captain Tim Forster had given us a horse called Dancing Ned – a real Christian of a horse, kind and reliable (which he needed to be if he were to form an effective part of my riding education) – and in that first go over Chris's schooling jumps we went upsides Ian McKie, at that time champion point-to-point rider. But my own ineptitude was easily equal to the skills of my equine and human tutors, and after one jump I managed to get my reins over my head and round the small of my back. Jumping two more fences like that and then pulling up is not the safest – nor the most stylish – way to go about the job.

The next man to attempt the impossible was Nick Gaselee, during the six months that Charlie Egerton and I spent with him after I'd left Eton. Nick himself had been a fine amateur jockey, but Fred Winter had been the greatest of his generation, and the chance to learn from the master was too good to pass up. When I asked the Guv'nor what I could do to improve my strength in riding a finish, he told me that the best jockey in a finish he ever saw was Johnny Gilbert, who was by then an instructor at the British Racing School in Newmarket. Fred drove me up to see him, and Johnny plonked me astride a saddle on a bale of straw, with a pair of reins tied to the nearby post – this was well before the development of those sophisticated equine simulators jockeys commonly use today – and it was in this unlikely setting that I tried to learn the finer points of riding a finish.

My first rides for Fred were on the mad Fionnadoir, who was partly owned by my mother and whom we've met earlier in these pages. It was useful to have a horse in the yard co-owned by Mother, as The Guv'nor could hardly refuse to let me loose on him, but in due course I started to come in for rides for other owners at Uplands.

The first 'outside' ride I had for Fred was at Ascot on a horse named Joe Sunlight in a handicap hurdle in December 1983, but thereafter my riding career was far from meteoric, principally due to the fact that the stable amateur was Fred's assistant Oliver Sherwood, an exceptionally good jockey in the Winter tradition of having assistants who were gifted in the saddle: Oliver's predecessor was Nicky Henderson.

During this period my exploits in the saddle were regularly chronicled by the 'Blowing Stone' column:

Charleston Brooks is a man of many parts – one of them quite small, so the wenches of the Valley tell ... Charleston's antics on his long-suffering nag Fionnadoir have caused much merriment in the Valley – after one disastrous outing his trainer sent the beast for an MOT to establish that brakes and steering were present ...

Some hefty bets were landed at Newbury on Friday when the noble C. Brooks and Fionnadoir completed their first chase in one piece.

Betting in the Valley was intense as to which fence they would part company at. The cross fence was favourite and drew wry post-race comment from the intrepid Brooks: 'They looked like collecting second time round.'

But those of us who have recently studied Brooks have become aware of his steady improvement and took all the 20's about him completing ...

WHERE ARE THEY NOW?
Mrs C. Brooks of Burford writes to say: 'Where is my son, Charleston?

'I used to see his name quite regularly in the papers, even scrambling home on the occasional winner, but I have not seen it for months – is he all right?'

He certainly is, Mrs B., although rides have been a little thin since his nag Fionnadoir went in for a service in November.

Charleston continues to labour at Uplands, spending much of his spare time attempting to earn his sixer's stripes with the 12th Lambourn Cubs, which he believes will qualify him for the Grand Military Gold Cup . . .

I strongly recommend employing Charleston this hunter-chase season. As he says: 'It's quite fun engaging me.

'I make people laugh in the paddock and on the racecourse, and I'm good at receiving a bollocking – I've just finished an advanced course under Miss H. Knight at Lockinge.'

My problem was simple. I wasn't as good as Oliver, though this brutal fact of life did not diminish the hurt when I was twice jocked off Glyde Court in the Kim Muir Chase at the Cheltenham Festival – in favour of Simon Sherwood in 1985 and John Queally in 1986. On both occasions Glyde Court won.

The second year the loss of the ride hit particularly hard. By that time I was riding a good number of the stable's runners in amateur races, a reflection (or so I thought) of the extent to which my skills had improved. I learned about losing the ride after a terrible day at Doncaster, when I'd been badly cut up in a hunter-chase by some aggressive northern amateur intent on seeing this soft southerner off his patch, and had then missed riding the winner of the bumper through some breakdown in communication. Already extremely pissed off, I received the news that John would be riding Glyde Court at Cheltenham, and my mood sank even lower.

That evening I was staying at my mother's in Oxfordshire. She went out to dinner, leaving me alone with my depression, and I went on a complete binge. I ate and I ate and I ate – a loaf of bread, a whole chicken, three tins of baked beans, a packet of cereal, six packets of biscuits. Getting that lot into my system did not lift my depression, but I thought I'd better make myself sick.

First came the tried and trusted method of sticking my fingers down my throat. Nothing happened.

There was a pheasant hanging up outside the kitchen, so I plucked a feather from the bird and stuck that down my throat. Nothing happened.

Then I remembered the James Herriot book *All Creatures Great and Small*. A dog eats some rat poison, which is flushed from his system by making him violently sick after drinking soap suds. So I made myself half a pint of Fairy Liquid and swallowed it. But still nothing happened – except that for forty-eight hours I felt so comprehensively ill that to this day the merest whiff of washing-up liquid makes me nauseous.

For any rider, from the rawest amateur upwards, being jocked off a horse – that is, being replaced by another rider – hurts like mad, but it takes on a particular sharpness when the horse involved is part-owned by the rejected rider! That happened to me with Deep And Even, a horse I owned in partnership with Barry Brazier. I'd won on Deep And Even at Newbury and then fallen on him at Nottingham, on account of his habit of jumping a fence cleanly and then tripping over. I knew that Fred had not been impressed by how the horse and I had parted company at Nottingham, but it was none the less a shock to walk into the Winters' house one evening to find Fred and Barry Brazier discussing riding plans for the horse – a horse, remember, half of which I owned – and agreeing to put another amateur rider, Tim Thomson Jones, in the saddle for his next race. I was incandescent with anger that all this was being done behind my back. In due course Deep And Even did the same thing with both Peter Scudamore and with Ben de Haan, so perhaps it was more the horse's shortcoming than my own, but being replaced on him made me seethe.

Scu was the great professional and I the raw amateur, but all men were equal under the withering onslaught of a Fred Winter bollocking, and after racing on the middle day of the 1987 Cheltenham Festival – soon after the problem over Deep And Even – we were both given the full treatment. We had both committed what in Fred's eyes was the cardinal sin at Cheltenham – not putting the horse in the race with a chance. Fred was a great believer that the way to ride Cheltenham was to bounce out of the starting gate spitting fire, and this applied with extra force during the three days of the Festival, when every horse is tuned to run for its life, every race run at a very fast pace: be slow at the start and you'll never get into the race.

Fred's bollocking really hit home that day, and while changing to ride Observe in the Foxhunter Chase the following afternoon I said to Scu: 'The old bastard won't be able to tell me I haven't given this one a ride . . .' Determined not to be the victim of another tongue-lashing, I popped Observe out of the gate straight into the lead and made all the running to land the biggest win of my riding career.

Observe had been a very good servant to the yard – it was on him that John Francome rode his 1,000th winner – but as he got older had rather lost his form, and we concluded that he'd become fed up with the game, so we'd sent him hunting and then hunter-chasing to sweeten him up. I'd ridden him a couple of times before Cheltenham and had been careful not to take the whip to him, as it was hardly the ideal Cheltenham preparation for an old horse whose enthusiasm needed rekindling. Nor, I thought, was Fred's decision to run him at Lingfield a couple of weeks before Cheltenham when I was sidelined with a broken collarbone, though it was doubtless a measure of how the Guv'nor rated his Cheltenham chance that he thought he'd better pick up a poor Lingfield hunter-chase on the way.

Despite the tender handling we'd given him, we had no way of knowing how far Observe could rediscover his old form, and we were not confident: as I left the changing room to go out to the paddock, Ben de Haan assured me that I had not a hope in hell! Looking at his rivals, you had to concede that Ben had a point. The Irish-trained No Other Way was favourite, with three other exceptional hunter-chasers in Border Burg, Attitude Adjuster and Eliogarty also preferred in the market to Observe, whose starting price of 14–1 just about reflected his chance.

This was the famous day when the running of the Gold Cup was postponed for an hour and a half after a snowstorm had enveloped Cheltenham racecourse, and the Foxhunter was the race immediately before the big event. At the start of the programme there was no problem, but by the off-time of the Foxhunter, second race on the card, the snow had started to fall, and for a while there was some question about whether that race would go ahead as scheduled. We assured the starter that there would be no problem, and duly set off. For the first circuit the snow came down so heavily that I couldn't see a thing through my goggles and had to pull them down . . .

Having worked out the very sophisticated tactic that if I made as much of the running as I could then at least I wouldn't be bollocked for not putting the horse in the race, we made every yard. On the first circuit I was convinced that I wouldn't be in front for very long so I might as well enjoy it as long as I could, and with Observe jumping out of his skin and never putting a foot wrong, it was an exhilarating experience.

One of the central planks of Fred Winter's Cheltenham philosophy was that on the final circuit you had to be handy at the water jump, as you did not want to be making up ground on the uphill run which follows it; nor did you want to be having to make up too much ground coming down the hill, so kick for home from the top of the hill and hope for the best. When we reached the top of the hill second time round Observe was still going well enough, but I was waiting for the other runners to come sweeping past me. Then I gave him one reminder with the whip and a couple of kicks in the belly, and he picked up so well that I started to think serious thoughts of at least getting a place.

Coming down the hill we were still going strong, though Alan Hill on Border Burg loomed up on the run to the third last before his effort suddenly gave out. As Observe swept into the straight with two fences to go the only serious danger was Katie Rimell on Three Counties, and going to the last she posed a serious threat. She went to pop the fence while I gave my horse a kick into it. He came up and got away from her – though I landed unbalanced and very nearly fell out the side door. If I'd fallen off then the humiliation would have been such that I'd never have gone to a racecourse again, but I managed to find a piece of Observe's mane as a lifeline, righted myself and proceeded to push on up the hill. Three Counties came back at us in the last hundred yards but we held on to win by a length and a half.

The next ten minutes were the best of my life. There was the walk past the front of the packed stands, the huge thrill of winning the best hunter-chase of the season on such a good old horse, and for one of Fred's most loyal owners David Bott; and there was the reception that Fred himself gave me, with an air of quiet satisfaction. He told the press later that he'd had more natural jockeys in his yard – I wasn't going to take issue with that – but he'd never had one who worked so hard, and it was that aspect of the win which gave me most satisfaction. Although I was well aware that I'd never be the best jockey in the weighing room, I'd tried and tried to improve my riding, and finally it had come good on the greatest stage the sport can provide.

After I'd changed Fred bought a bottle of champagne in the Turf Club tent, and we consumed this with Di Winter and my mother in a quiet corner while the 'Will it be run?' drama of the snow-threatened Gold Cup went on outside. By the time The Thinker charged up the hill to beat Wayward Lad I was well past caring about the Gold

Cup, but the yard had another runner that afternoon in Half Free in the Cathcart Chase – due to be run at 5.15 and actually off at 6.26. After Half Free and Scu had galloped out of the gloom to give the stable a rare Festival double, we repaired to the box of Half Free's owner Sheikh Ali Abu Khamsin. I have a particular memory of sitting well into the evening in a corner of Sheikh Ali's box having a drink with Scu, who like me had responded to the Winter bollocking the day before in the best possible way by riding a winner.

It had been one of those wonderful days when everything comes right.

People's attitudes to me as a jockey had changed a bit after I won on The Reject, one of the more enigmatic inhabitants of Uplands. Ridden by John Francome, The Reject had fallen in the Arkle Chase at Cheltenham in March 1985, and in his next race, at Chepstow the following month, fell again and managed to add insult to injury by trampling all over his rider as he got up. For John it was the last straw, and he wrote in his autobiography: 'I am not superstitious as a rule but I took this as a hint that it was time to pack up and so that's what I did.'

The Reject returned to Cheltenham for his first race of the following season, a chase for amateur riders. Well aware of the horse's quirks (he didn't get that name for nothing), I decided to provide minimal interference and sat as quiet as a mouse, with the result that the horse ran as sweetly as could be and won well.

If only my partnership with The Reject had ended

with that race my stock as a rider would have risen considerably, on the basis that if I could win on the horse that had ended J. Francome's career then I couldn't be so bad after all. But unfortunately The Reject and I were to meet again, with a less happy outcome.

It was the culmination of an unbelievably awful week. On the Tuesday I'd screwed up the entries – I'd gone through the wrong week's programme! – and, having confessed to a highly unimpressed Guv'nor, I had to drive at the crack of dawn on Wednesday morning to the Weatherbys office in Northamptonshire, and from there go straight to Fontwell to ride my favourite headcase, Fionnadoir, in a novice chase. Fionnadoir started odds on but fell, taking such a heavy tumble that he lost an eye. The following day The Reject was running at Cheltenham. Ben de Haan was due to ride him, but Fred had decided that if the weights went up I'd take over and use my seven-pound allowance. I was hoping that this wouldn't happen as I was not inclined to push my luck with The Reject, but sure enough the weights went up, and I had to ride. At the same fence he'd fallen at with John in the Arkle, The Reject buried me.

Although you would not think so to hear some of the comments which fill the air any afternoon in the average betting shop, the standard of riding over hurdles and fences has never been as high as it has been over the last few years, with riders of the quality of Richard Dunwoody, Tony McCoy, Graham Bradley, Norman Williamson and Jamie Osborne showing skills which precious few of their predecessors from previous generations could have matched. With the advent of blanket coverage of racing through SIS, the Racing

Channel and so on, every individual ride can be scrutinised closely, not only by the jockeys themselves but by trainers. As a consequence, standards have risen enormously, and the average jockey is much tidier and much more effective than in the past.

Having said that, the best jockey I've ever seen in action is undoubtedly John Francome. He was quite superb at presenting a horse at an obstacle, and while his finish left a bit to be desired in his early days, by the time he grew into a mature rider he was as strong as anyone at the business end of a race. Above all, John had brains. He knew when to go miles wide to find better ground, or when to pull up a horse if he felt it had gone wrong. Occasionally he'd have a personality clash with a horse, and there were some horses who were simply not suited to his manner of riding. When he rode Fifty Dollars More, for example, he was always trying to get him to settle rather than let him bowl along and make the running, which suited the horse better. If the horse does not want to do what the jockey wants it to do, it's an unhappy experience for both parties.

John was stable jockey when I first went to Uplands and already well established as one of the best jump jockeys of all time, but there was not then – and there has never been – any side to him. He took everyone as he found them, be they a duke or an ordinary man in the street. Around the yard he was a constant source of joking, especially when he did one of his famous impersonations of the Guv'nor. He was always very pleased to help anybody out, and it became common for young jockeys in the yard to go up to his house with a video of their latest ride for him to go over with them – not because he was high and mighty about his own skills, but simply because he wanted to help and encourage them.

With characteristic foresight and good sense, John had started building his own yard in Lambourn while still riding, and I had a horse with him named Village Draper. John and I shared the view that horses should do a great deal of long, steady cantering before going into faster work, and every other day, after finishing my morning's work at Uplands, I'd go up to his yard and take the horse out for six miles or so cantering to get him fit. It seemed to do the trick; a short while before he was due to run in his first race we brought Village Draper to Uplands, gave him one piece of stiff uphill work and knew we had him spot-on. As luck would have it (as I wouldn't have won on him) I got injured before his race, and Ben de Haan had the ride when Village Draper made a winning debut at Hereford on 3 March 1984 – my twenty-first birthday. We celebrated that night at the Oxford restaurant run by former jump jockey Paul Barton.

John's retirement in April 1985 after that disagreement with The Reject was a blow to Uplands, and he was an impossible act to follow. For the first year following his departure most of the stable's rides were shared between Ben de Haan and Jimmy Duggan, but the horses were not right that season and both had a rather lean time of it, through no fault of their own. By the summer of 1986 Fred was anxious to recruit a new stable jockey, and there was no more obvious choice than the reigning champion Peter Scudamore, then first jockey to David Nicholson at Condicote. Fred admired Scu greatly, because he was so tough: you got up his inner at your peril, as plenty of rival riders discovered, and this was very much Fred's philosophy.

Scu was an integral part of the Uplands operation when Fred had his accident, and he and I formed a very close relationship. Winning the Champion Hurdle with Celtic Shot – his first win in one of jump racing's Big Three races – drew us closer together. But as time went on, Peter wanted to make sure he was riding as many winners as he could, and we knew we couldn't keep him for ever once he'd started to form an attachment to the Martin Pipe stable.

Certain jockeys have certain strengths, and Scu, the ultimate professional, would never get off to a bad start. Some used to carp that he wasn't the greatest stylist, but for me he was as stylish as he needed to be. We worked closely together at Fred Winter's for years, and it struck me that Scu (just like, in his own time, Fred Winter) never much enjoyed the necessary routine of schooling.

The opposite applies to another jockey closely associated with Uplands, Graham Bradley. Brad loved schooling. If I asked him to jump a horse the wrong way over a fence – that is, taking off from the landing side – in order to sharpen up his concentration, Brad would happily do so. Florid, for example, wouldn't concentrate on his jumping, so Brad took him up to the schooling ground above Lambourn when no one was around and jumped him over everything in sight – hurdles the right way and the wrong way, fences likewise. In all he must have taken that horse over forty obstacles, and it did the trick.

Brad and I did a lot of work with Yogi Breisner, the doyen of equine jumping teachers. Some thought it a dereliction of duty for a trainer to get someone else to train his horses to jump, which always struck me as a fatuous attitude. Trainers bring in specialists to shoe their horses or analyse blood tests: why not use a specialist to hone their jumping ability? It's not only the horses who have benefited from Yogi's expertise: Brad and Jamie Osborne would both admit that he's fine-tuned their riding of a horse into an obstacle.

Richard Dunwoody, who on Easter Monday 1999 rode the 1,679th winner of his career and thus overtook Scu as the winning-most jump jockey of all time, is the rider who invites the closest comparison with John Francome. Although he did not ride often for Uplands, I've long been a great admirer of his ability to present a horse at a fence, his strength and his all-round horsemanship.

Not all jockeys can be such paragons, of course, and there are plenty of bad jockeys riding alongside the good. The bad jockey will let a horse meet a fence all wrong; will be a poor judge of pace and either go too fast, thereby letting his horse burn off too much energy too soon, or go too slow and lie too far out of his ground; will not have the nous to pick the best piece of ground; and will not be a team player. That last attribute can be crucial, as all the best trainer–jockey relationships are based on a shared goal and the teamwork that goes alongside it. Graham Bradley and I spent ages walking the courses before a lot of races to decide where the best ground was to be found and put a great deal of thought into how the race should be approached.

Owners, understandably enough, like to think that the stable jockey is a team player, and little in racing causes such bad blood as the jockey who chops and changes his plans, who gets off one horse to take what appears to be a better chance on another. When Peter Scudamore's priorities came to lean more and more towards Martin Pipe and less towards Uplands some of the owners grumbled, with the result that we started to look around for a jockey whom we knew would be able to ride for us more regularly. Scu understood the situation perfectly well and helped in the search for an alternative.

I'd known for years that Graham Bradley was an exceptionally gifted and sympathetic rider, but there was no denying that his career had been one of ups and downs, including some high-profile brushes with the racing authorities. As a young jockey in 1982 he was given a two-month ban for going into the betting ring at Cartmel and winning a few quid on an odds-on chance he fancied. Five years later he was suspended for three months for failing to ride out a horse at Market Rasen. Barney Curley complained to the Jockey Club that Brad had stopped Robin Goodfellow at Ascot, but he was exonerated. In 1989 he was again up before the disciplinary committee over his riding of Starjestic at Southwell: there was a suggestion that he had deliberately jumped off the horse, but photographic evidence showing that Starjestic had got his feet into the open ditch made it evident that Brad's unseating was perfectly straightforward, and again he was cleared.

Many of the downs, moreover, had not been of his own making. He had ridden for Michael Dickinson – and won the famous 1983 Cheltenham Gold Cup for him on Bregawn, first home of the Dickinson runners who claimed the first five places – and then Michael stopped training jumpers. He had ridden for Michael's mother Monica Dickinson, and she had retired.

On more than one occasion either my mother or myself was given clear indications that Brad was a marked man at the Jockey Club, and in many ways this encouraged me to take him on. If he was under such scrutiny it was unlikely that there would be any funny business.

My intention was to offer Brad the job during the end-of-season meeting at Perth in May 1990, but the relationship got off to a false start. I'd asked him to come and school a horse at the racecourse but he'd spent the previous night out on the town with Steve Smith Eccles and didn't show up for the schooling session. I was furious – so furious that after saddling Melicus, my first Brad-partnered runner that day, I went off to the bar rather than go and talk with him in the paddock. (The owners of the horse were not there.) After this aggravation I decided to let him sweat for a while and didn't offer him the job until late summer.

My head lad Brian Delaney got to hear about Brad's non-appearance at Perth, and when Graham arrived at Uplands at 7.32 a.m. – two minutes late – to report for his first morning's schooling he had quite a surprise.

'Morning, Bri!', he cheerfully greeted the head lad.

'Don't you "Morning, Bri" me! It's "Morning, head lad" to you and you're late. If you think you can come wandering in here late and keeping us waiting, you'll find that either I go or you do and I doubt it's going to be me.'

This approach worked a treat, and Brad was never late again.

Brad came with a certain amount of baggage and that had to be a concern to me – and to the owners, some of whom were uncomfortable about the appointment. So when we were discussing his becoming stable jockey I was quite explicit: mess around on one of my horses and there'll be no second chance. He gave me his word that he'd never let me down – and he never did. But the trouble with that baggage is that it won't go away, and Brad has long had to fight that reputation. In all his years as my jockey, until the episode with Man Mood there was only one race in which it seemed that Brad's baggage was going to be added to: the notorious – and outrageous – case of Marouat at Southwell in January 1992, which confirmed to me that the knives were still out for him.

Marouat, a gelding owned by Lady Joseph, had started his career with us encouragingly, but by the middle of 1991 was becoming inconsistent, and showing signs that he was losing interest in the game. In September 1992 he won a chase at Uttoxeter, then ran down the field at Cheltenham in October and came third at Doncaster in December. We could tell that he was losing interest (*Timeform* had his measure, describing him as 'not one to trust') and started to think that we should get rid of him, so we decided to run him in a really terrible race called the Scrooge Claiming Chase on the all-weather track at Southwell in January, since if he caught someone's eye there he could be 'claimed' for a specified amount and we'd be shot of him.

He did catch the eye, but for quite the wrong reasons.

Having drifted in the market from 6–4 out to 3–1, Marouat – whom Brad rode only because the Wolverhampton fixture the same day was abandoned – turned in a thoroughly mulish display. He was reluctant to line up with the other runners at the start, and although he eventually jumped off in second place he soon lost his position: after four fences he was back-pedalling, after six he was tailed off, and after the seventh Brad gave up the unequal struggle and pulled him up. It all seemed straightforward enough to me – but not to the racecourse stewards at Southwell, who hauled Brad before them and fined him £500 under the rule designed to punish non-triers.

There certainly was a non-trier in that race, and his name was Marouat. And we soon found out why.

I was not at Southwell that day but had watched the race on television. I was incensed by the stewards' decision and immediately announced that we'd lodge an appeal on Brad's behalf with the disciplinary committee of the Jockey Club, whose chairman was then Sir Piers Bengough. In my fury I issued a volatile and totally over-the-top statement to the press:

> I have written to Sir Piers Bengough inviting him to choose a race to run Marouat in next week in which they can put a jockey of their choice on the horse and we will see what happens then. The whole thing is ludicrous – you need only look at the form book to see this horse has simply lost his form and there is nothing we can do about it.
>
> We will fight this all the way. This is a slur on me, it is a slur on Brad, and it is a slur on the horse's owner, Lady Joseph. I am really furious about it.
>
> I watched the race on SIS and you could see that Marouat didn't even want to line up at the start. We can't find anything at all wrong with him – we wouldn't run him if we could – and we have

tried everything to rekindle his enthusiasm. But he has lost his form and mentally he just doesn't seem to want to know any more. To describe him as unenthusiastic would be diplomatic.

I am amazed that the stewards think he didn't run on his merits and I take it as a personal insult. They haven't fined me but I feel it is very damaging for me because it casts completely outrageous aspersions on my jockey and I don't like that very much.

Fast forward to the Jockey Club headquarters at Portman Square in the West End of London. The press had rallied behind Brad. Brian Giles in the *Daily Mail* wrote how the enthusiasm of the stewards

certainly outstripped that of the horse Bradley was riding . . . I don't think there was anything Bradley could do about the situation, and I really do not believe it would be in anyone's interest to allow the fine to stand. I say give the man a chance and let him get on with the good job he has with Charlie Brooks.

That was typical of the backing we were getting; but the support of the press was one thing, the matter of overturning the stewards' decision quite another.

Brad and I turned up at Portman Square with his solicitor Peter McCormick and were ushered in to face the disciplinary committee. The three members of the committee sat on one side of the table, with the three of us facing them, and the stewards' secretary, whose role was to advise on finer points of the rules, at one end.

We watched the Scrooge Claiming Chase over and over and over, a million times from a million different angles, and I was beginning to think that we were heading for defeat. They'd got it into their minds that Brad was cheating, and that was that. (And no mention was made of my challenge to Sir Piers!)

Then the stewards' secretary asked the committee to consider yet another view of the race which, he said, clearly showed Brad pulling the horse back with one hand while simultaneously pushing him forward with the other.

Now, I don't know how much direct experience of race-riding that fellow has, but to perform what he was suggesting Brad was up to would take some doing, and after this extraordinary observation the mood of the committee seemed to change.

The session was brought to a close and we were asked to wait outside while the three good men deliberated. Peter McCormick thought we'd lost, but when we were called back in after about half an hour kicking our heels, we were told that the appeal had been upheld.

'No hard feelings, old chap?' said the stewards' secretary outside the room, and though my instinct was to reply robustly, I still held a licence and thought it wiser to bite my tongue.

I was pleased that the decision had gone our way, but it was no more than the righting of an absurd wrong, and given Brad's less than spotless track record I was determined that a potentially very damaging situation – 'Oh, Brad's still at it' – be nipped in the bud. The episode did show that appeals can be upheld by the Jockey Club; in an ideal world, though, I do believe that there should be an ultimate form of appeal to a panel that is free of connections with the Jockey Club.

In the event, Marouat himself made clear what the real problem was. We discovered that he had a severe problem with a bone in his foot which was about to deteriorate rapidly: the kindest thing to do was to put him out of his misery.

Those were the stories which made the headlines, but the true measure of Brad's character was provided by less public moments such as the generosity of his reaction after the 1995 Hennessy Gold Cup, won by Dean Gallagher on a horse Brad could have ridden.

Richard Dunwoody may have passed Scu's record, but it's surely only a matter of time before his total is in turn beaten by Tony McCoy, whose short but phenomenal career has lit up jump racing over the last few years. He's had his share of problems over his use of the whip, but he's so strong that I have a hunch that if jockeys weren't allowed to hit horses at all, Tony would have an advantage rather than a disadvantage over the other jockeys. In his sheer will to win he reminds me of Peter Scudamore in the early days, and he's still improving. Some pundits worry that his dedication and single-mindedness will cause him to burn out in a few years' time, but such fears are probably unfounded. With him, as with all jump jockeys, so much depends on avoiding injury. A jump jockey falls every dozen or so rides, and by the nature of the game some of those falls are going to cause injuries. The more rides you have, the more likely you are to have the serious falls which shorten the career.

One of the reasons Graham Bradley's career has gone

on so long is that he's had remarkably few falls – and one of the reasons for that is that he has enough sense of self-preservation to know when to pull one up.

Though as I write this, I can think of one horse that he probably wishes he hadn't . . .

8

OF HORSES
AND
HORMONES

I T WAS A PIECE of grey gristle about the size of a golf ball, and I'd just dug it out of a dissected horse's head during a veterinary course at the University of Bristol.

'What's this?' I asked the lecturer.

'Oh, that,' he replied: 'That's the horse's brain . . .'

Contrary to what many racing fans like to think, horses are not very intelligent creatures, and anyone closely involved with them – even to the point of betting on them – does well to remember that.

The ideal racehorse is one who will eat, sleep and shit in regular patterns, and will do his best at exercise and on the racecourse. You do not necessarily want too much intelligence alongside that sort of reliability, as a horse over-endowed with grey cells might well conclude that racing itself is not for him. In many ways the most intelligent racehorses are the ones who won't go into the stalls, and won't exert themselves, and it often seems to be the case that the more intelligent the horse, the more he frets and worries his energy away, thus rendering him less useful as a racing proposition.

Temperament is all part of the make-up of the Thoroughbred, and a certain amount of spirit is highly valued. But nervousness, though closely related to spirit, is a dangerous facet of a horse's temperament, since nervousness has a very direct effect on performance: a horse that gets very worked up at the races is unlikely to give his best on the track.

This is why it is very important that young horses should not have hard races. You can spoil a young horse by pushing him too hard too soon. You may win your race, but that horse may never be the same again, and may never reach the level he would have attained had he been brought along gently and been allowed to enjoy his racing. It's not dissimilar from how we should treat children: if a child does something well and is rewarded with a beating, is he going to want to repeat the experience? Similarly, if a horse gets to associate trying hard with having his arse whacked, is he going to keep trying hard?

I feel strongly that young horses should not be whipped, which is why I'm so against the concept of running a championship bumper – a race on the flat for young jumping horses – at the Cheltenham National Hunt Festival. Many horses get mentally ruined by being pushed too hard in bumpers, and the very notion of a champion-ship bumper seems to me to be quite against the original purpose of National Hunt Flat races.

But whatever the horse – young or old, nervous or placid – it's an uphill struggle to get him fit and well enough to run, since the bald fact is that a large proportion of the racehorse population of this country is ill most of the time. If betting-shop punters thought a bit less about how bent they think racing is and a bit more about the fact that half the horses they are backing have recently been sick, will soon be sick or currently are sick, they might not be so keen to lump on their money.

To get an expert opinion about this crucial problem besetting modern racing, I went to see Barry Allen. Based in Martin Pipe's yard in Somerset, Barry analyses blood samples for Martin and for other trainers and, after a lifetime researching methods of assessing equine health, has to be the man who understands the situation better than anyone.

Barry Allen was a pioneer in the early days of blood testing, and spent years at the Equine Research Station at Newmarket developing techniques to monitor the blood's reaction to infection. He was persuaded to move to Lambourn, where I would happily sit in his laboratory all day and listen to him expound on the basis of his work: 'You have to know what's normal. If you don't know what's normal, you can't know what's abnormal.'

Equine blood consists of 40 per cent red blood cells and 60 per cent plasma, and when the horse exerts itself the spleen empties the equivalent of 50 per cent of the circulating red blood cells into the bloodstream, thereby hugely increasing the supply of oxygen to the muscles. This makes the blood very thick (a human would not be able to walk with that level of viscosity in the blood), but the horse's blood cells are very flexible, which prevents the blood solidifying. This all sounds highly complicated, but there is an obvious practical application for a trainer, and Barry was always telling me about the dangers of overtraining a horse. The line between a horse being fit and being tired is a very thin one, and when the horse is overtrained the red blood cells become less flexible, the blood circulation does not operate as efficiently as it should, and less oxygen is transported from the lungs to the muscles.

Overtraining produces cortisol, which burns off sugar, and a horse running with a low sugar level will soon get tired. Overtraining is also a cause of stress in a horse, and when a horse gets stressed one type of its white blood cells (lymphocytes) is reduced in number, while another (neutrophils) is increased. Hence the crucial importance of blood tests – which can detect such imbalances – in knowing whether the horse is fit to race.

According to Barry Allen, there are three reasons why horses suffer loss of performance (apart from individual problems such as injury): infection in the yard, incorrect feeding, or contamination of bedding. Of these, by far the most problematic is viral infection, which has plagued the racing industry over the years. The trouble with infection is that there may be more than one type of virus circulating around a yard at any one time, and in that situation illness is impossible to shake off. One viral agent may be in the yard for four or five weeks, and the horses will come right once it has departed. But if there are two the problem may persist for four or five months, and if there are three or more the horses might not be right for years: horses catch one after the other and then get reinfected.

Feeding is a vital consideration, since to function properly a horse must have the correct mineral balance in its body. If there is a wrong balance – for example, not enough calcium or potassium – he will not be able to perform. An additional worry in recent years has been chemical contamination, and chemicals sprayed on to hay or oats or finding their way into the drinking water may well be a source of loss of performance, while dusty bedding might contain spores which cause inflammation of the lungs and the generation of large amounts of mucus.

It all adds up to a pretty alarming picture; so what conclusions can Allen reach about the overall health of our racehorses?

'The racehorse population is definitely more unhealthy than it used to be. Respiratory disease is now endemic in racehorses in training, in breeding stock and in livery yards. More horses have it, so there's a greater chance of catching it, and to make matters worse every virus mutates into sub-groups which prolong the problem. Twenty years ago it was unheard of for jumpers to have the virus, and now it's everywhere.'

When you consider that Barry Allen is familiar with the nature of the blood flowing through the veins of Martin Pipe's horses, it's sobering to hear him admit that's he's given up backing horses: 'I find football easier – I got three score-draws in a treble last week.'

Barry's thoughts about the sickness of the racehorse population are echoed by Brian Delaney, head lad at Uplands since the day Fred Winter started there: 'Years ago when Mr Winter was training, the good horses would all run to within five pounds of their best form all season, once they were fit. Now it seems that everyone's horses are much more in and out.'

In Brian Delaney's opinion, the culprit is the compulsory annual flu vaccination – 'It can't be right to mess around with a horse's immune system' – and I strongly share his scepticism about 'fluvacs'. For a couple of years I used to break the Rules of Racing by not giving some of my horses flu vaccinations – no doubt a very naughty thing to do, but I found a vet who shared my opinion and who would enter the vaccinations into their passports without actually administering them (in any case, the compulsory annual flu jab does not protect horses for a whole year). My feeling was that if a horse was exposed to flu, the vaccination would hide the symptoms but not stop that horse feeling pretty ropey, and in that case I would be working a horse suffering from sub-clinical flu, which wouldn't do it any good at all. I would much rather they coughed and had dirty noses so that I could see they were wrong and back off them.

After two years of not vaccinating half the yard, there was no obvious difference between the amount of flu suffered by each group, which seemed pretty convincing to me. My scepticism was further boosted when I sent blood samples from ten horses who had not been vaccinated to the laboratory in Newmarket: they reported that one of the ten seemed not to have had the flu jab as the level of antibodies against flu was very low, but they didn't mention the other nine.

Administering drugs to a horse to counter an illness is one thing. Administering drugs to enhance performance is quite another, and provides one of the biggest challenges facing the authorities that run racing.

I strongly believe that there are trainers in Britain who are giving their horses drugs to get an edge, and it's easy to understand why. Drug abuse is widespread in sports where the financial gain is minimal compared with horse racing, and the combination in racing of big money and human nature makes it inevitable that there will be skulduggery. The more to gain, the greater the skulduggery. So either every racing professional is a freak of nature and a paragon of virtue and the sport is completely clean, or they aren't and it isn't.

Drug testing in world sport first came to prominence after the death of English cyclist Tommy Simpson in the 1967 Tour de France, and cycling has remained in the limelight as far as drug abuse is concerned. In 1989 alone eighteen cyclists – former and current – died of heart attacks. The drug which cycling has brought to prominence is EPO – erythropoietin, a naturally occurring hormone secreted in the kidneys. It acts on the bone marrow to stimulate production of red blood cells, and in human medicine is used to treat anaemia linked with HIV infection and for people with chronic kidney failure. Since it is naturally produced, there is no satisfactory test for its presence in the body. International cyclists now have tests to measure the volume of red blood cells, and if a competitor is registering higher than 50 per cent he is stood down for his own safety.

There has been plenty of evidence of the use of EPO in cycling, including the seizure of a huge quantity of the drug in the boot of a team car at a customs point, but it is only one of a rapidly changing 'cast' of drugs worldwide. Canadian sprinter Ben Johnson was caught using Stanozolol at the Seoul Olympics in 1988, after which two other athletes wanted to withdraw: they were persuaded to compete but neither was placed. A triumph for dope testing? Not according to Dutch coach Henryk Kraayenhof, who was reported as saying: 'If anything, Ben Johnson's getting caught promoted drug use. He won.'

More recently a Chinese female swimmer was caught red-handed by customs authorities at Sydney with containers conveniently labelled 'growth hormone' in her luggage; and at the Atlanta Olympics in 1996, where there was urine testing but not blood testing, a drug so new it wasn't yet on the banned list was detected in the samples of athletes from Russia and other East European countries: this drug had been used by the Russian military to keep troops alert and to help them adapt quickly to extremes of heat and cold.

For top sportsmen, the temptation to use performance-enhancing drugs is very strong. In 1995 a poll of 198 sprinters, power lifters and other assorted athletes in the USA asked these two questions:

(1) You are offered a banned performance-enhancing substance with guarantees that (a) you won't be caught and (b) you will win. Would you take that

substance? Answer: 195 said yes and just three said no.

(2) You are offered the same substance but this time (a) you will not be caught (b) you will win every competition for the next five years and then die from the side effects of the drug. Would you take that substance? Over half the sample still said yes.

If that's the nature of the modern-day sporting spirit, how can you take it for granted that the sport of horse racing is clean? It is common knowledge that when the Jockey Club brought in dope testing in Britain in the early 1960s, more than one trainer was known to be using steroids on his horses and had a quiet tap on the shoulder from the Jockey Club to the effect that he should stop.

At the root of the matter are the questions: what is acceptable and what is not, and why? When I was training it was common practice to ask the vet to give the occasional horse a shot of the steroid Nandrolin if that horse looked not to have done too well when it came in at the beginning of the season. In that case one would naturally have to be careful not to run the horse too soon and risk failing the dope test, but so long as the drug was not detectable on the day of the race, no rule had been broken.

On a couple of occasions I used what is known in Australia as a 'milkshake' – a large dose of sodium bicarbonate which is an alkali solution – administered via a stomach tube a couple of hours before the race. The theory was that this solution would act as a buffer to the lactic acid produced in the muscles during a race: by neutralising that acid, the muscles would be prevented from tiring so quickly. I tried this on Espy, who tended to show higher than normal muscle enzymes in his routine blood tests: the first time we used it he broke the track record at Newbury and the second time he bolted up in the Fairlawne Chase at Windsor. (We picked those two tracks as they're close to Lambourn, and we could give him the milkshake two hours before the race and still get to the course on time.) There was at the time no rule against using this substance, but as the vet who first told me about it said: 'If they've banned it in Australia it must be doing some good!'

It would be unfair, though, to suggest that the authorities over here have been asleep as far as keeping the list of prohibited substances up to date is concerned, and the introduction of dope testing of horses in training in their home stables means that nowadays a proper explanation would be required if, say, Nandrolin were to turn up in a sample. The Jockey Club has also banned horses being given anything other than water in racecourse stables.

I have often wondered whether I would have used an illicit substance on my horses had it been offered me. Working on the assumption that had I been offered it, it probably would have been used already by others, I probably would have gone for the option of exposing the use of it and creating a level playing field. If that were not possible (or I felt I was going to end up in concrete boots) I would probably have given it to my horses so long as I was convinced that they would suffer no long-term health consequences. I'm aware that my competitive nature has always made me want to get an edge, which is a logical and understandable human weakness. But this all remained in the realm of the hypothetical, since I was never offered anything.

If trainers are using drugs now, what do I think they're using?

EPO has to be a prime candidate. The point of using EPO is that the more red blood cells a horse has, the more oxygen can be carried to its muscles, and as oxygen debt is the biggest limiting factor to performance, more oxygen means that a horse can compete at a higher level for longer.

Some experts argue that its use is widespread, others dismiss the idea. Australian racing has long been awash with innuendo and rumour that the drug is being widely used there – and if that's the case, then a supply for British stables is only a flight away. Off the record, equine experts speak of its widespread use in the southern hemisphere (it comes in two dosage forms – 4,000 ml and 10,000 ml – and costs anything from $200 to $1,000 per injection), and top Sydney vet Nick Kannegieter has gone on the record to make clear his opinion that the use of EPO in horses is common, though not through vets. He also believes that testing for EPO is a long way off.

Those who are not convinced that EPO would be an effective way of blood-doping a horse point to the special qualities of the equine spleen, which stores huge amounts of blood when at rest. But when adrenaline is released into the bloodstream the spleen empties the fresh blood into the system, thus 'blood doping' naturally. The infusion of yet more red blood cells through an injection of EPO might then cause a cellular 'traffic jam' and make the blood too thick.

In any case, EPO is not the only candidate. EST – Somatrophin, a 'growth hormone' – is in some quarters considered a more serious threat. Equine growth hormone is now manufactured synthetically in Australia and is acknowledged as being effective for the treatment of older horses suffering muscle loss and for regenerating tendon tissue in young horses.

Significantly, urine tests – the only tests conducted on British racecourses – do not show up either EPO or equine growth hormone, and it is undeniable that post-race blood testing is needed if this business is to be sorted out. It is surely no coincidence that the International Olympic Committee has decided to bring in blood testing for the Olympic Games in Sydney in 2000. A true deterrent to the use of such substances in racing would be to introduce blood testing, and combine this with a practice of freezing samples and keeping them for up to ten years against the improvement of detection methods. 'Drug cheats' know that testing methods are always improving, and would not relish the thought of their past catching up with them. (Since the first edition of this book was published the Jockey Club has brought in a very limited programme of blood testing before racing at minor meetings. This is a step in the right direction, but it is not enough. A reluctance to carry out tests at big meetings is worrying, and wheeling out 'cost and logistics' as reasons for not freezing the samples is even more disappointing.)

The Jockey Club may have moved with the times and introduced the dope testing of horses in training, but they still allow horses to race in this country who are not subject to such tests. It is difficult to think of any other international sport which would allow that situation: there would be uproar in athletics if our athletes were tested in training and then had to compete against rivals from other parts of the world who weren't. Whichever way you look at it, allowing horses from the USA or Dubai, countries where they do not have testing of horses in training, to race over here does not make for a level playing field. But when I asked Christopher Foster, Executive Director of the Jockey Club, about this he became quite shirty with me: 'You're casting aspersions,' he claimed angrily.

Casting aspersions? I was no more doing that than is the Jockey Club itself when going into a racing stable and taking samples. But his reaction did make me wonder whether I'd hit a nerve.

The other main area where horses and drugs come together is in the perennial problem of 'bleeding'. There are probably more theories about 'bleeding' than any other aspect of the racehorse, and no one has ever had all the answers to the problem – though for plenty of trainers the immediate action to take with a horse who tends to break blood vessels is the judicious use of the drug Lasix.

Lasix is a diuretic which stops horses bleeding. Nobody knows for certain why it works, but it does seem to be very effective; the problem with it is that it is among the prohibited substances listed in the Jockey Club Rules, and any horse found by the post-race drug test to have it in his system will be disqualified. Ten days before a race is about as close as one normally dares to administer Lasix without its showing up in the dope test, though some trainers risk a gap of as little as four days.

The theory is straightforward. If you work a horse hard on Lasix to stop it bleeding, and then do not push him hard in between then and his race, that horse can be trained without the continual risk of haemorrhage.

Whether horses should be allowed to race on Lasix remains a contentious subject. In most states of the USA (New York is the major exception) the drug is allowed, on the basis that if you know a horse has a problem, why not use the right drug to solve that problem, in much the same way as you would antibiotics against an infection? It can be very distressing for horses to bleed, so why is it not fully justifiable to prevent that happening?

On the other hand, there is a strong argument for not allowing the use of Lasix. By masking the problem rather than removing it, you will allow some horses to win races that without the drug they would not have won, and that success may lead to their being used for breeding, and thus pass on the proclivity to bleed (which can be hereditary). Over time, this will weaken the breed. There's something in that argument; but since most bleeding is the direct consequence of the horse having had some sort of infection, rather than a genetically inherited trait, the argument for taking the humane route of allowing horses to race on it may gather force.

As anyone who has ever dealt with horses will know only too well, their ailments can become the bane of your life. Those ailments can also land you with a date at Charing Cross police station . . .

9

A BRUSH WITH
THE LAW

I HAD ONLY ONE runner at Warwick on Tuesday 5 November 1996: Man Mood.

In the morning papers he looked to have little chance of beating either of his two rivals – Drumstick and Mine's An Ace – in a very poorly contested handicap chase. Of the fifteen newspaper tipsters whose selections for that race were listed in the *Racing Post*, only one went for Man Mood, and I was not inclined to dispute the experts' opinion.

Man Mood had long been a problem horse. When he came under pressure he started to choke, which hindered the supply of oxygen to his lungs. It was a bit like switching off the supply of petrol to a car's engine, though rather worse: at least with a fuel-starved car you don't lose the steering. In bad cases a horse so afflicted will act as if drunk, as the muscles malfunction due to lack of oxygen.

In order to get to the bottom of Man Mood's problem I sent him in the summer of 1996 to Geoff Lane at Bristol University's renowned veterinary department, where he was galloped on a treadmill with a camera in his throat in an attempt to identify where the problem was occurring. But this revealed nothing, so it was decided not to operate.

When we ran him at Worcester first time out in the 1996–7 season the problem clearly had not gone away, but we felt that if we could find a race with a small field he might be able to relax by bowling along in front and so avoid choking. Problems like this are often caused when a horse gets tense and it was doubtless worth a try, but I didn't hold out a great deal of hope as he still gurgled at home when he worked on his own.

We had also tried tying his tongue down. This involves pulling the horse's tongue forward and tying it to the jaw by wrapping a couple of feet (in length) of ladies' tights round, the theory being that if the horse's tongue is well forward in the mouth the soft palate will be kept in the correct position: the choking is caused by the soft palate flopping in the inhaled air, and tying the tongue prevents this happening.

We hoped for the best, but did not approach the Warwick race with any confidence at all. In the race-course car park I met Norman Williamson, who was due to ride the expected favourite Mine's An Ace, and he told me that his horse had trodden on a stone and had been withdrawn. This left us in a two-horse race, but still I couldn't muster much enthusiasm for Man Mood's chance of winning.

When the on-course market for the Oliver Cromwell Chase opened Man Mood was favourite to beat Drumstick: given the horse's problems I thought this was ludicrous, and advised anyone who cared to enquire that I didn't think Man Mood would win.

One of those people was 'Dodger' McCartney, a professional backer of National Hunt horses and a particularly nice man whom I was always only too happy to help when I could. That day I advised him to avoid mine: Man Mood was not reliable, and even in a weak two-horse race was not a betting proposition. I even advised Man Mood's owner Julian Robbins, who stood to win about £4,000 in prize money if his horse won and a little more than £1,000 if he was second, to have £500 on Drumstick to balance his risk. He decided he didn't want to, which was fair enough.

When Brad pulled up Man Mood with a mile to run, leaving Drumstick to win unchallenged, I was disappointed but not that surprised. Nor was I surprised that the stewards held an inquiry. They seemed perfectly happy with the explanation which Brad and I put forward: the horse had choked badly and lost his action, and in the circumstances pulling him up was the only sensible course to take. I did register, though, that the betting intelligence officer – an official whose job it is to sniff out unusual patterns of betting in the racecourse ring – was hopping up and down a bit.

The matter did not end there. The Jockey Club announced that it would be holding its own investigation. After answering all the questions about the horse and the race yet again, I was pretty put out to be asked if I would supply the Jockey Club with a copy of my mobile phone bill for the period around that race. I discussed this position with Andrew Cohen, who as owner of the yard owned my mobile phone, and we agreed that it would be best to hand it over. The Jockey Club – presumably someone in the Security Department – subsequently leaked to two national newspapers the fact that they'd been examining my phone bill, to see what sort of shady characters I might have been talking to.

In due course the Jockey Club completed its investigation and I was told that the matter had been dropped. I was also given the impression that no evidence of irregular betting on the race had materialised. (Three years later I found myself sitting next to Chris Bell, managing director of Ladbrokes, at a lunch at Ascot, and took the opportunity to ask him whether his company had been unhappy about the race in any way. 'Not in the slightest,' he replied. 'In fact we took more money on your horse than on the winner.' What about the other bookmakers? 'I'm not aware of anyone being unhappy.')

After the completion of the Jockey Club investigation I had assumed that the matter was sorted out, and remained of that opinion until I walked into Charing Cross police station that Friday in January 1999.

The day after my arrest and visit to the cells I was due to go off with Miriam for a couple of weeks in the Caribbean, and I was buggered if I was going to let a small matter like being arrested screw up those plans. So we went, thereby avoiding the immediate aftermath of press comment and speculation. By and large the press were very fair to me, though one newspaper did run a story along the lines: Brooks arrested in connection with race-fixing investigations ... four out of five jockeys arrested during the investigation have ridden for Brooks ... Brooks has had well-known financial problems in the past. It was a shitty article and the insinuation was loud and clear.

On my return to England I found myself a new legal representative. While the man from our family solicitors had been fine for the emergency on the day of my arrest, I had been accused of a criminal offence and felt that I should engage a top criminal lawyer, even if it meant parting with £300 an hour for his services. You only have one good name in life, and I had to pay whatever it cost to preserve mine.

I had been recommended to Monty Raphael at Peters and Peters, and on going to see him mentioned my girlfriend Miriam Francome.

'That name rings a bell,' said Monty. 'About twenty years ago I represented a man named John Banks, and there was a Francome involved in that' – referring to the Jockey Club disciplinary enquiry in 1978 in which John Francome was accused of supplying information to the bookmaker John Banks. 'I lost,' Monty continued.

'Marvellous!' I thought. 'That's all I bloody need.'

My next bail date was set for mid-March, but again travel plans were a factor: I was due to be in South Africa on the date suggested, so it was moved to later in the month; then, after Brad had been for his next bail hearing, I was told that I was to present myself at Charing Cross police station at 1 p.m. on Tuesday 13

April – the same day that Brad would next be appearing. (Ray Cochrane had long since been eliminated from the police investigations.)

Between my first appearance at Charing Cross and my second I had no contact with the police at all, though that's not to suggest they'd lost interest in me. One day I received through the post a neatly typed but anonymous note:

> The police are watching you.
> Act normal.

I couldn't work out the significance of the date for my next appearance coinciding with Brad's. I had been told by Monty Raphael that I shouldn't speak to Brad: it wouldn't look good. This was difficult, as we were in constant touch in the normal course of events; so, after initially thinking that if I was being given £300 an hour advice I should pay heed to it, I found myself changing my mind. As far as I was concerned neither of us had done anything wrong, and I was damned if I was going to skulk around like a criminal. In any event, Brad and I did not have a huge amount to talk about regarding the case, but when we did meet, over dinner with Miriam, Brad's girlfriend Bob (yes, I know that's confusing, but that's her name) and trainer Paul Cole, the only interesting thing to emerge from comparing notes about our interrogation by the police was that we both appeared to have been asked the same questions.

As a sop to the lawyer and what I thought was a fair compromise, I never met Brad on his own. Given the paranoia brought on by being arrested out of the blue, it wouldn't have surprised me if we'd been tailed anyway. I'd heard so many stories about phones being tapped that I simply assumed someone was listening in to my conversations, and I was advised on good authority that my calls would be monitored just before and just after I was questioned.

In this atmosphere of suspicion and fear of phone-tapping, you can imagine just how amused I was when Jeremy Graham, one of my oldest friends, called soon after my arrest:

'Thank God you made all that money fixing those races – it'll pay for the lawyers. Hwah hwah hwah!'

'Thanks, Jeremy. But before you tell your next little joke, bear in mind that you're probably sharing it with the Serious Crime Squad.'

Monty Raphael's job when preparing for my reappearance at the police station was not made easier by the fact that he had not been representing me on my first visit there, and that his request for a tape of my interviews with the police back in January had been refused. Thus he did not know exactly what I'd already been asked.

He seemed to take all this in his stride (I suppose the £300 an hour helps) and when we turned up at the police station on 13 April my instructions were simple: they want to question you further, and the only answers you are to give are 'Yes', 'No', 'I don't know' or 'I can't remember'. And if there should be a pregnant silence after any of my answers, I was not to fill the void by waffling on.

The long and the short of it was that, innocent or guilty, contact with the law is a game, and you have to know the rules.

Monty's last words to me as we walked up to the front entrance of Charing Cross police station were: 'They've been very uncommunicative – expect the worst.'

I was taken aback by this, and it set me thinking about all those stories you hear about the real criminals getting away with it and some innocent little bloke carrying the can. Was I about to become that innocent little bloke?

My trip to Charing Cross coincided with the first day of the Craven Meeting at Newmarket (also, to my great chagrin, with the Heythrop point-to-point, normally an indelible entry in the Brooks diary), so it was no surprise that most self-respecting racing journalists had better things to do that day than wait around in the rain for me to meet my bail. But what the press corps lacked in quantity it made up in quality – David Ashforth of the *Racing Post* and Lydia Hislop of the London *Evening Standard*.

Brad had been due at the police station two hours earlier than me, at eleven o'clock (he must have been late, judging from the time he passed me on the M4 doing about 300 m.p.h.), but there was no sign of him when Monty Raphael, his assistant Daniel Smith (a dead ringer for Charlie Swan) and I arrived. We were quickly summoned through to the inner office, where two policemen went into a huddle in the far corner. Monty had warned me that I would be rearrested, but instead one of the policemen said to him:

'We have no further questions for your client. He is free to go.'

That was it. No further questions. Over. Exonerated. Free to go.

This felt very odd, and in a curious way I was disappointed. There were a few things I wanted to say, to get on the record. But there was no opportunity.

Actually, they did have one further question for me: 'Do you want to take your stuff with you?' They had five fertiliser sacks full of documents taken during the dawn raid three months earlier, and now they wanted me to lug these away with me. Having no car with me, and no overpowering inclination to help the police at that moment, in however trivial a way, I declined, and they told me to pick them up from New Scotland Yard within a week.

After the dust settled I thought a great deal about the police officers in the Serious Crime Squad who came to our cottage at dawn, turned my life upside down and probably ruined my reputation. I can't dislike them. They were doing a job, and no doubt doing it as well as they could, and you have to respect them for that. Plenty of people inside racing thought that the police had been crashing around in our sport, making fools of themselves, and – to some extent – of the Jockey Club, who had involved them in the first place. Racing is a particularly cocooned world, with its own language and way of doing things, and outsiders can't just walk in and understand it. There may be something in that view, but it never struck me that the police in this case were stupid: they were doing their job as well as they could.

I was still pondering my reaction to the police when they brought the five fertiliser bags full of papers back to the cottage in East Garston, and over a cup of tea I suggested to them that my arrest had been totally unnecessary. I had answered honestly all the questions they had put to me, and they could have had the same answers without going to the trouble (for them) and the humiliation (for me) of my being arrested.

One of them replied that I had to understand that the police do not necessarily believe that everyone they arrest is guilty.

'Tell that to Joe Public,' I said. 'As far as I'm concerned my reputation is fucked for ever.'

'Oh, I wouldn't worry', said the policeman. 'These things are soon forgotten.'

I was grateful to the police for bringing the papers back to East Garston – after all, it saved me from flogging up to New Scotland Yard – and that night was telling a friend at dinner what nice people they were.

'God, you're naïve!' he said: 'Busy detectives don't run a delivery agency. They probably bugged your cottage when they raided it and were coming back to retrieve the bugs.'

That possibility had never occurred to me; but it makes you think, and inevitably after an experience like that you ponder what it was all about. In spite of the fact that the Serious Crime Squad hit our place before dawn, their search of the cottage was cursory – they acceded to Miriam's request that they keep clear of her own desk. I was questioned on one occasion only, and had my personal papers confiscated for three months: being without essentials like my phone book and my diary was not convenient. Surely if they had anything on me they would have questioned me again at the very least?

So what *was* it all about? Perhaps it was all connected with the culture of racing, and the currency which operates within that culture – a currency called information.

People bet according to information. If they don't bet, racing collapses because it has no money. The ante-post market on big races would hardly exist at all were it not underpinned by the flow of information, and bookmakers have been thriving on this for years. Everyone in racing – from Stewards of the Jockey Club to stable lads – deals in information.

But, horses being horses, information is usually wrong – which is why most punters are skint and most bookmakers are rich.

The market on Man Mood's race at Warwick was said to have shown 'irregular betting patterns', but the fact is that, with very few exceptions, bookmakers in England are not renowned for laying big bets, and the chances of getting a hefty whack on the outsider of two in a crappy chase at Warwick in November are nil.

Being arrested rather than just questioned made the whole affair very public, and whatever the law of the land may say about the accused being innocent until found guilty, that's not the way most people see it. The arrest cost me a great deal of work at a time of my life when I was trying to build a new career, which was aggravating and damaging – though the *Daily Telegraph* and the Racing Channel stood by me.

I was especially annoyed about the effect which all this was having on my mother. She never acknowledged that she was upset, but then she wouldn't. On the plus side, during this period I saw a great deal more of my sister and her children, and in a way the experience drew us closer together.

Needless to say, once I was cleared I was bombarded with messages from people saying the wrong thing –

'Congratulations: you must be so relieved.' But relief was not my emotion when I'd just blown a five-figure sum on legal fees and loss of earnings. And congratulations – for what? For having had my name dragged under suspicion? For having a man who worked for me having his own reputation called into question for behaving like a true professional on a problem horse that I trained?

I was not relieved; I was bloody angry.

It was Charlie Egerton who restored my equilibrium and my sense of humour. The day after my appearance at the police station I was at a sale in Newmarket, feeling slightly paranoid that people who did not know me well were not sure what to say. Not so Edgie:

'Morning! So it looks like you won't be sharing Jonathan Aitken's turkey this Christmas after all.'

There was a much less humorous side to that day at Charing Cross. The police issued this statement:

Graham John Bradley, 38, a jockey, has been charged that on or before the 5th of November 1996 within the jurisdiction of the Central Criminal Court he did conspire with others to win for himself or others from bookmakers sums of money through wagering on the event of a horserace, the 3.25pm at Warwick on November 5, 1996, by fraud or other unlawful devices in that together he agreed that Man Mood, ridden by him, would not win the said race.

Brad was bailed to reappear at committal proceedings some two months later, and a few days after being charged was informed by the Jockey Club that his licence to ride was being withdrawn pending the outcome of the case. At the committal proceedings in early June he was informed that the charge had been dropped – an outcome which I had never doubted.

My view of how Brad rode Man Mood at Warwick has always been clear. To those who were quick to criticise him for being in such a hurry to pull the horse up, and to those who smelled a rat not because of the circumstances of the race but because of the identity of the jockey, I would ask this: have you ever been on top of a horse in a steeplechase with another mile to go when that horse starts gurgling his head off and losing his action?

I have – in a chase at Cheltenham on a half-brother to Brown Chamberlin called Brolin. At the top of the hill, three fences from home, he started choking, and felt as if he was drunk as the oxygen failed to get inside him. Being an inexperienced amateur keen to impress Fred Winter, I kept going. It was only luck that made us meet the last three fences in our stride, and had we not done so we'd have had a desperate fall. You don't get to be Graham Bradley's age and still very much in one piece by doing stupid things like that. But Brad has long been a marked man, and during the Jockey Club investigation into the Man Mood race it became clear to me that he was the one they really wanted to get, not me.

As far as I'm concerned Brad has done nothing wrong. The only evidence I was ever confronted with was the police telling me that 'someone says you fixed the race', and there was not a thing I ever saw or heard which made me think other than that he was completely innocent.

This whole affair brings up yet again the question asked by anyone who has ever read a Dick Francis novel, anyone who has ever backed a losing horse and thought the jockey didn't try quite hard enough, anyone who has ever glimpsed the shady-looking characters who seem to attend every race meeting:

How straight is horse racing in Britain?

Within racing it was widely assumed that the Jockey Club had called in the Serious Crime Squad to investigate suggestions of race-fixing since the police have greater powers of searching and questioning, and therefore that the Jockey Club itself obviously did not think that the sport was straight. And the investigation into both jump racing and the Flat indicated that both codes were under suspicion.

Amid so much rumour and innuendo, hard facts are thin on the ground, but there are a few. It has been shown that in March 1997 two horses in National Hunt races were doped to lose: Avanti Express, ridden by Jamie Osborne, at Exeter and Lively Knight, ridden by Leighton Aspell, at Plumpton. The riders of both horses spent many unpleasant months as part of the race-fixing enquiry before being released without charge, but the suggestion that any jockey would get up on a horse he knew to be doped is grotesque, since the chance of a drugged horse doing serious damage to itself and/or its rider is considerable. One can safely assume that no jockey would contemplate doping any horse, and in any case the rider only meets the horse minutes before the race so would have very little opportunity to administer anything.

It is hard to believe that those two races were the tip of an iceberg, since (a) 'stopping' drugs are fairly primitive and likely to show up on dope tests, and

(b) National Hunt racing is not a suitable medium for fixing: even if you stop one horse you can have no guarantee of the result of the race, as horses can fall or be brought down. Leaving aside doping, it is much easier for a jockey deliberately to lose a race on the Flat than over jumps, since on the level races are run at a faster pace and there is more bunching, making it much easier for a rider to encounter interference or traffic problems. The stewards watch races very closely and are aided by filmed recordings from all sorts of angles, but none the less only a complete innocent would deny that the occasional horse does not achieve its best possible position.

The Serious Crime Squad will have been looking for just that: serious crime. They will have known all about the law but less about the language and the culture of racing, and at the root of that culture we come back to the staple currency of information. It is against the Rules of Racing for jockeys or stable staff to pass on information about horses to anybody other than that horse's owner or trainer, but everyone in racing knows that it happens all the time. If every jockey who ever passed on information and every steward who had ever received information were to be warned off, racecourses would be pretty sparsely populated places.

The Serious Crime Squad do not deploy valuable time and resources merely to look into possible irregularities with regard to a couple of piddling races. There must be a bigger picture, and it can be no coincidence that there is now open talk among the upper echelons of racing about suspicions that the sport is being used to launder money from the international drugs trade. Even the Senior Steward of the Jockey Club has not denied that one of the reasons why bookmakers' racecourse pitches have become hugely valuable, and have changed hands for large amounts of money, may relate to the movement of drugs money.

There is always a bigger picture.

These are murky waters, but while it's easy for us to say that overall British horse racing is the cleanest in the world, I'd be very surprised if that weren't the case.

That opinion, however, has to be qualified by considering just what you mean by straight. Only a fool or a complete innocent would think that every horse in every race is doing his level best to win, but the reason why this might not be the case is not skulduggery or criminality: it's handicapping.

In any system that involves handicapping horses there will always be connections who look at a horse's rating and conclude that he isn't good enough to win off that handicap mark. Therefore, if they wish to win with that horse at some point in the future, either they have to improve the horse or they have to get his handicap rating lowered. That's a basic part of racing, and getting a rating down by losing a few times is simple enough. Run the horse two gallops short of his peak fitness. Run him two furlongs short of his optimum distance. Run him on the wrong type of ground, or the wrong type of track, or have him ridden in the wrong way: make too much use of him, or have him held up when he's better striding on. While the core of racing is based around handicapping horses, people will always want to get their horses better handicapped, and will always find ways of doing so. The knack for the punter is to see it happening, and take advantage when that horse is ready to win.

It suits mug punters to think that racing is bent, since that way they are protecting themselves from the knowledge that they are mugs: they like to think that they lose not because they are wrong, but because the sport is so corrupt that they cannot win. Your average betting-shop punter seems to think that every race is fixed, yet they carry on betting. You have to wonder about the intelligence of that . . .

You also have to wonder about the intelligence of some individual punters. Shortly after Suny Bay ran his heart out to finish second under top weight in desperate going in the 1998 Grand National, I received a letter:

<u>C.B.</u>
YOU KNEW EARTH SUMMIT WAS GOING TO WIN G. NATIONAL WHEN YOU TOLD THE PUBLIC 'SUNY BAY' WAS GOING TO WIN – ALL PRE-ARRANGED WITH JOCKEY CLUB – BBC – ETC. ETC.

IF YOU EVER DO THIS AGAIN I WILL GET SOME-BODY TO BURN YOUR STABLES IN LAMBOURN.
<u>DON'T EVER TRY IT AGAIN</u>
<u>BE WARNED</u>

My correspondent unfortunately forgot to sign his name, but if he'd care to get in touch with me I'll let him have the copyright fee for reproducing his letter in this book.

10

A NATIONAL PASSION

W HAT A DIFFERENCE A **year makes.**
On Grand National Day 1998 I was at Aintree
to saddle up Suny Bay, one of the leading fancies for
the race.

On Grand National Day 1999 I could not even bear to
watch the big event.

After all that had gone on since Suny Bay's heroic second in 1998, his second consecutive year as runner-up,
I just wanted to put as much space as possible between
me and the race. By Friday, the day before the race,
I'd reduced my choices for what to do on National
Day down to two: go and watch Oxford United play
football, or go and watch the sheep. On reflection,
these alternatives came down to about the same thing,
so I went to the Manor Ground, Oxford, to see the local

heroes continue their brave but doomed resistance against relegation from the First Division by playing fellow strugglers Bury. Oxford lost.

So did Suny Bay, and I have to admit that it was with very mixed feelings that I crammed into the tiny betting shop inside the Oxford United ground to watch the National on a small television screen. Luckily no one else in there (and there weren't very many – Oxford United supporters had other things on their minds that afternoon) seemed to know who I was, so I was not bothered by anyone asking me how I felt.

How did I feel, as I saw Suny Bay fade on the run down towards Becher's Brook on the second circuit, getting further and further behind the leaders and eventually finishing thirteenth? I felt disappointment – for the yard, for Brad, and most of all for the horse – and yet a fair amount of relief. For Suny Bay to have finally won the National when I could have been still training him would have been very difficult to swallow.

The Grand National first crept into my consciousness on that visit with my grandmother to the betting shop in Moreton-in-Marsh when I was six, when a lifelong passion was sparked. I've ridden in the race and trained several runners in it – including one of the most gallant losers.

From the moment the Grand National first got its grip on my young imagination I was desperate to take part, and I finally got my chance in 1987. My sister's then father-in-law was the colourful Irish actor Richard Harris, and he had asked me to buy him a horse to run in the National after I'd ridden his brother-in-law round the dining room one Christmas beating him with the fire poker. I duly went to Ireland and bought him Insure, a very good and reliable chaser who had won the Irish National in 1986 when trained by Pat Hughes. But once I'd brought Insure back to Uplands, Richard did a disappearing act and reneged on the deal. I was livid.

The following Christmas my mother, concerned that this was still rankling and knowing that Richard would be in the party, asked me: 'Now you won't say anything to Richard, will you? We've all got to spend Christmas happily together.'

'OK, Mummy,' I sighed.

Richard duly arrived at the house and came straight up to me.

'Charlie – sorry about that horse.'

'No problem, Richard. Not your fault.' It was my mother's turn to sigh – with relief. Then I continued: 'Not your fault at all . . . that you're a jerk.'

I'd got that off my chest, but there was still the problem of what to do about Insure, which was solved when he was bought by my mother and a couple of her friends, Mike Gover and Eileen Cowan.

From the day he arrived in Fred Winter's yard Insure was wrong, and we continued to have terrible problems with him. He was plagued by lameness, and I seriously began to wonder whether he was the same horse that I'd ridden when I went to buy him in Ireland. But thanks to the genius of Mary Bromiley, the legendary equine physiotherapist based near Lambourn, we managed to get him to Liverpool for the 1987 Grand National, and he looked an ideal conveyance for my assault on the course.

This was not the first time I'd had a go at the Grand National fences. I'd ridden Gay Tab in the Fox Hunters' back in 1984 – ending up in the ditch before Becher's Brook, still on my horse – and, as on that earlier occasion, was accompanied to Liverpool by my mate Fritz. Although I was struggling with my weight I decided that a liquid dinner was in order, with a little fish as ballast, and by the time I went back to my hotel room for a salt bath I had put on four pounds in two hours.

Salt baths were my preferred method of losing weight quickly. Unlike in a sauna, where you sweat out salt, which leaves you feeling weak, lying in a salt bath sucks water out of you via osmosis and leaves the salt inside your body. (Technical bit: osmosis is the exchange of fluid through a semi-permeable membrane [your skin] from a weaker solution of salt [your body fluid] to a stronger solution of salt [bath water saturated with salt].) Through this method I lost as much as I could on the evening before the race, but it was going to be impossible to do the weight and ride on even a remotely comfortable saddle, so when the time came to weigh out I cheated, and weighed out with a tiny saddle a good ten pounds lighter than the one on which I ended up riding the race. I managed to switch them before Mick Cullen, Fred Winter's travelling head lad, came to the weighing room to pick up the saddle. I was well aware that I would be in hot water if I got round – and thus have the discrepancy revealed when I came to weigh in – but since the likelihood of that was extremely remote, it was a bridge I was happy to cross once I got to it, and I certainly didn't fancy tackling the Grand National course on a saddle not much bigger than a postage stamp.

Fred Winter, who as the rider of two Grand National winners and the trainer of two more was something of an authority, told me that it was crucial to get a good start. Even though the distance of the race is four and a half miles, they go very quickly early on as every jockey tries to get the position he wants, and a good start is thus vital if you're not to get pushed to the back. In order to encourage me to take his advice, Fred bet me £20 that I wouldn't be first across the Melling Road, halfway between the start and the first fence. It was a close call but Insure and I had a head advantage over Ben de Haan on 1983 winner Corbiere, and after the race Fred duly paid up.

The old horse gave me a great ride. He was in the front rank all the way down to Becher's Brook, and as we approached the obstacle was leading upsides another horse. I glanced across to my right and saw that this was Lean Ar Aghaidh – popularly known as 'Lean On The Aga' – who was trained by Stan Mellor and owned by my old friends the Tullochs. About ten strides short of Becher's I was thinking, 'If I fall out to my right here and bring him down they'll never invite me back to their grouse moor again,' and then about five strides short I thought, 'I don't think I should be worrying about shooting right now.'

Passing the stands after a circuit Insure and I were still very respectably placed in the leading half-dozen, and although he soon faded out of contention we did get round: last of the twenty-two finishers headed by Maori Venture.

Completing the course was a great thrill, but left me with the problem of how to get past the clerk of the scales without my transgression being found out. They rightly take a dim view of that sort of deception, especially in a race like the Grand National, and I was in line for a stiff rebuke and a hefty fine. This situation called for desperate remedies, and as I walked back into the weighing room past the scales I suddenly dropped everything bar my number cloth on the floor and plonked myself on the scales, beaming cherubically at the clerk. I'm not sure he was fooled, but he let me go.

There's a distinctly end-of-term feel to the Grand National meeting at Aintree. It's the moment when a long season starts winding down, and as it's one of the few occasions when we didn't have to charge back after racing for evening stables, we tended to have some pretty good times.

When Jamie Osborne and I were both young and unattached we shared a room at the Adelphi, and at the disco held in the hotel's basement there were usually a few young lasses game for a laugh. One evening we found a likely couple and suggested they might like to come up to our room for a drink. They were drinking what must have been a lethal mixture of Dubonnet and Bailey's Irish Cream, and by this late stage of the evening were having a certain amount of trouble walking on very high heels. It took a fair amount of steering to get them both into the lift, but all was looking well – though my aside to Jamie that 'Mine looks like Goldie Hawn' was met with some scepticism – until we reached our floor and started along the corridor.

'Fookin' 'ell, Lisa, this must be a posh place: they've even got wallpaper on the ceiling,' observed Jamie's escort, but at that moment Lisa's attention was locked not on the ceiling but on the floor: the excessive intake of Dubonnet and Irish Cream was about to have its revenge, and at that point the evening disintegrated.

A year later things didn't go much better. We had recruited Marcus Armytage to our scouting exercise and managed to get three young party animals up to our room. Unfortunately Marcus had had to tell a few porky pies to engage the interest of his date, and he had convinced her that he was Tom Morgan, who was riding the big-race favourite Dixon House. The television news was on in the corner of the room, and as Marcus's luck would have it an interview was being shown with – yes, Tom Morgan. We desperately tried to find the remote control but it was too late: Marcus's prey had seen the television and his cover was blown. The young party animals upped and left. End of seduction scene.

Some of the funniest moments I've had at Liverpool have been with John Inverdale, one of the great men of BBC Sport. John has a huge thirst for knowledge and doesn't let the grass grow under his feet: if he goes anywhere in the world to cover a sporting event he likes to get the feel of the place, which for the Grand National has meant our freezing on the 'Ferry 'cross the Mersey' to Birkenhead, skulking around Chinatown, being pious in Liverpool Cathedral or taking a trip back in time at the Beatles Museum. We've seen the balcony of the building which housed the White Star Shipping Line, from where the sinking of the *Titanic* was announced: the officials were so afraid of the anger of relatives of workers on the ship that they didn't dare come out of the building, and had to shout the news down from the balcony.

We've even been to a graveyard to see the grave of the Scotsman buried in a pyramid-shaped tomb: so keen was he on poker that he insisted his body was sat at a card table with him holding a royal flush when he died.

On the Friday night before the 1998 National, John and I were in the Beehive pub with BBC Radio racing correspondent Cornelius Lysaght, and were minding our own business when three very well-fed girls came up and asked if they could join us. Of course they could.

'So what do you do, then?' one of them asked.

Before anyone could answer I pointed at John.

'He's called Jake,' I said. 'He's an international gambler – that's why he's so brown. He flies around the world betting on horses, and is planning to clean up on the Grand National tomorrow.'

'Wicked, wicked!' the girls chorused in approval.

Then I indicated Cornelius.

'He's called Colin. He's a boring accountant from Bracknell. He does all the studying of the form book for Jake. That's why he's so pale: he doesn't see daylight very often.'

'Oh wicked, wicked! So what' – they asked me – 'are you doing with this lot?'

'He's called Charlie,' John perked up. 'He's a race-horse trainer and he's got one of the favourites for tomorrow's race.'

'Ah, fook off! – we're not that stupid, you know' – and off they went.

In a more professional context, I often worked with John Inverdale for the BBC on Grand National day, and it was in this capacity that I was at Aintree for the 1993 National, the infamous 'Race That Never Was'.

The fiasco of two false starts, the bedlam as officials tried to stop the race after one circuit, then the 'victory' of Esha Ness and the chaotic aftermath – that day may have been a disaster for racing, but it was a very stimulating moment for the broadcasters.

I was amazed by the reaction of the crowd on the racecourse. We were based in the unsaddling enclosure area, near the stewards' room, and I dread to think what might have happened if the police hadn't sealed off the weighing room. Tempers were running very high. Anyone wearing a bowler hat or in any way looking like they might be a racecourse official looked like getting torn to pieces by a lynch mob that was laying siege to the weighing room area. You could understand why the spectators felt cheated, but like so many disasters there were many contributing factors. I felt very sorry for Keith Brown, the starter. It never seemed to me that he did anything particularly wrong, but he got most of the flak at the time.

The 1993 running may have been a public relations disaster, but it was so typical of the whole ethos of the Grand National: it always throws up a good story. The year of the bomb scare, 1997, was possibly the most incredible of all, and this time I was more directly involved.

The Princess Royal was in attendance – earlier in the day she had unveiled a bronze bust of Peter O'Sullevan, whose final Grand National commentary was to be on that year's race – and security around the paddock was getting tight. I remember feeling that the pressure of training such a fancied runner as Suny Bay in the race was beginning to get to me, and thinking: 'Thank God it'll all be over in a few minutes' – and then to my amazement I saw the horses who were already in the paddock, the not-yet-saddled Suny Bay among them, heading for the exit. What on earth was going on?

Then announcements were made that the whole place had to be evacuated, and people started pouring out of the buildings and on to the course. At that stage no one seemed to realise that the entire course was being evacuated, and most assumed that after a while we'd be allowed back in and the race would be run. Coats were left hanging over the backs of chairs; the jockeys left the changing room in their colours and breeches. Even Des Lynam, doyen of BBC anchormen, was given his marching orders along with everyone else. Most interesting of all were the Tote ladies, stuffing bundles of banknotes into their knickers for want of anywhere else to put the stuff.

The racecourse stables were evacuated like the rest of the course, but two of my lads, Simon Molloy and Phil Sharpe, who looked after Suny Bay, refused to abandon the horses – many of whom had been left tied up with their saddles and bridles on, such had been the speed of the evacuation. Those two lads did a fantastic job: they attended to all the horses, rugging them up and making sure they had water and hay.

Later in the afternoon we were allowed back into the stable block: some of us decided to move our horses out, while others opted to leave their charges at the racecourse. I sent Suny Bay off to Haydock Park, where we were able to exercise him on the Sunday and Monday mornings. (I'm convinced that when the race was run on the Monday, this gave him an edge over the horses who had remained at the course: they had not been allowed out to exercise on Sunday.)

After seeing Suny Bay off to his billet at Haydock, I – along with thousands of others – was stuck with the quandary of what to do. All cars were impounded in the racecourse car parks, and although I was lucky in that the BBC had managed to hold on to my hotel room, I had no intention of just going back there. After a couple of hours aimlessly waiting around to see what was going to happen, I ended up in the Melling Road Working Men's Club, where a couple of chancers who were nothing at all to do with the club were charging people £5 a head to get in. Inside the club there was a party atmosphere very much to my liking – so much to my liking that I spent the entire next day there. In fact, I think they made me an honorary life member.

Back at the racecourse in the early evening, the situation was now a complete mess: no one was allowed to go back to their cars, and tens of thousands of people were facing the prospect of spending the night in just the clothes they stood up in – with the additional matter of having to find somewhere to sleep. It was not very long after my knee operation, and with all the standing around I was beginning to suffer, so some kind soul helped me out by offering me a nice big coat they had found, which kept me warm as evening approached. What I did not immediately realise was that this was a policeman's coat.

There was extensive coverage of the day's events on television that evening as part of *Match of the Day*, including easily recognisable trainer in knee brace and wearing large coat. In the early hours of Sunday morning

I was wandering back towards the hotel when a man came up to me.

'You're the fellow with the horse, aren't you? I like horses, so I'll give you some advice. Walk down that street with *that* on' – gesturing towards my coat – 'and they'll kill you. This is a no-go area on Saturday nights.'

What was he talking about? It all became a little clearer when on my return to the hotel I was greeted by a phone message from the local constabulary to the effect that unless the coat was returned by six o'clock further action would be taken. Apparently the chief constable had seen me in the coat on *Match of the Day* and was not amused. You have to sympathise: he'd had a hard day.

Back at the Adelphi there was a fair party under way, with about twenty jockeys dancing away in the night-club still wearing their silks. Since no one could get cars from the racecourse, they kept on and on partying – 'Have you lot come straight from work?' quipped the barman – and by Sunday night jockeys who at three-thirty on Saturday afternoon had been ready to ride at ten stone were weighing eleven.

Then the news came through that the race would be run on the Monday. Cue rush to the sauna.

On the Sunday afternoon the police allowed a BBC team back into the racecourse to check their equipment, and as part of that team I found my way back in – to be confronted with a very eerie scene, very like a ghost town. The televisions were all on, the lights were shining, lunches were left half eaten on tables, jackets still over the backs of the chairs. It was as if someone had waved a magic wand and all the people had vanished – which I suppose is exactly what *had* happened.

Prime Minister John Major, just embarked on the general election campaign which was to see him driven out of office, came up to give the race his support, and doubtless get a bit of decent PR for the campaign into the bargain. The Conservative blue of Andrew Cohen's colours on Suny Bay was an obvious attraction for a Tory, and as I legged Jamie – who still had a few red wine stains on his breeches from the previous two days' revelling – up into the saddle, Mr Major called out a cheery 'Good luck!'

'Thanks', said Jamie, 'but I think you're the one who's going to need the luck!'

11
CROSSING THE LINE

CROSSING THE LINE FROM trainer to observer of the racing scene, from insider to outsider, left me with very tangled emotions.

Apart from Suny Bay, there was one seriously good horse I'd had to leave behind: Barton, whom I had trained for Stan Clarke. I still have the letter I faxed Stan when we were starting to realise what sort of horse this was, but before he ever ran: 'Hope you had a good holiday. You've got a racehorse!'

I was not wrong. Barton hacked up in his first bumper at Huntingdon, only to be disqualified as he'd gone the wrong side of the wing of a (removed) hurdle, and was then second to a good horse in Muskhill in another bumper at Bangor-on-Dee. I thought that he could go all the way to the very top, and it was with mixed feelings that the season after I quit I saw this horse, now trained in the north by Tim Easterby, become one of the most exciting young hurdlers in years, with a scintillating victory in the Royal & SunAlliance Hurdle at Cheltenham. At least he went to a good trainer who did a fine job with him, as he wasn't totally straightforward.

On the other hand, I was relieved to know that I never need hear the words 'trachea wash' again . . .

Crossing the line also gave me the opportunity to reflect on various aspects of racing which are more difficult to consider rationally from close up.

Take the administrative structure of the sport, and especially the role of the Jockey Club. When I was a trainer I had to be very careful what I said in public about that noble institution: after all, they had my licence – and thus my livelihood – in their gift. I've never been against the Jockey Club, but I do think that some parts of it are better than others, and that they undersell themselves. For instance, Tony Goodhew, Director of Racecourse Services, has done outstanding work getting racecourses to improve the ground and forcing them out of the 'we've always done it like this' mentality. But one problem endemic in the sport is that there are too many bodies running it. The BHB are elected to run racing and yet have little power. The racecourses call the shots as they own the media rights – the pictures transmitted from the racecourses – and the Jockey Club has influence through ownership of racecourses via its own Racecourse Holdings Trust. Racing can never achieve its potential with such a divided power base, in the same way that no company or industry can be run along these lines. As the racecourses have only themselves to worry about, while the BHB represents the whole industry, it is the BHB and not the racecourses that should control the media rights.

The BHB should be all-powerful, and in chairman Peter Savill there is at last a figure with the energy, abrasiveness and clear-sightedness to move racing forwards. Some sneer that his financial goals for racing are unattainable, but if he fails, you can kiss goodbye to racing ever getting the deal it needs if it is not to remain grossly underfunded.

To my mind, Peter Savill is the potential saviour of the sport; but another man who deserves our eternal gratitude is the Marquess of Hartington, who during his time as Senior Steward of the Jockey Club had the vision to set in train the reforms which brought about the formation of the BHB in 1992. 'Stoker' Hartington did a truly remarkable job in the face of much internal opposition, but he stuck to his guns and dragged racing's administration out of the Dark Ages.

Strife between the various bodies – which seems to rumble on year after year – is as dangerous as in an army consumed by internal discord even as its enemy bears down upon it, and for racing that enemy is very easily identified. When push comes to shove, racing's overpowering problem is the stranglehold in which it is held by the bookmakers. In spite of the fact that racing produces an attractive and successful product – the spectacle of horses and jockeys flat out to be first home – someone else takes away the money it generates.

There are two types of bookmaker. Those on the

racecourse are, as far as I'm concerned, welcome to their profits. They add great colour to the racing scene, and contribute in their own way to making the sport fun. But the big chains of betting shops have never been fair over what they put into the sport from which they gain their turnover. It's difficult to blame them: they struck a great deal when off-course betting was first made legal in 1961 and have stuck doggedly to it. But what is particularly galling about this situation is that ever since that monumental change in 1961 racing has allowed the bookmakers to behave like cuckoos, pinching all the choicest eggs from the nest, without doing anything about it. This has been a political game: the bookmakers realised early on what a golden goose racing was, and figured that as long as they kept lobbying Parliament effectively – on both sides of the House – no government would be inclined to upset the status quo.

It would appear that they were right. The bookmakers were much more astute and streetwise than the Jockey Club who were running racing: it was almost like a sharp bunch of spivs against the landed aristocracy, and it turned out to be a very one-sided contest. The bookmakers realised what huge profits they could make from people gambling on horse racing, and the powers that ran racing either didn't realise what the score was or chose, for whatever reason, to turn a blind eye.

As far as the overall health of the sport is concerned, there is still a certain amount of complacency. What's so wrong? Lots of people own horses so they must be fairly happy: where's the problem?

The best way to appreciate the difficulties which racing is storing up for itself is to consider the case of two young men I employed at Uplands: 'Chuck' Norris and Tony McKeown. They are two of the very best stable lads of their generation, and after I left Uplands stayed on with Simon Sherwood. And what do I now hear they're going to do? Leave racing – Tony to expand his gardening jobs, Chuck to enrol on a computer course. With people of that quality seeping out of the industry, who is going to look after the Thoroughbred population in years to come? Probably young girls happy to do the work for poor wages as they love horses; but once they get married they'll move on. Surely a skilled lad or lass who rides well should be earning enough to get married, have a car, pay a mortgage on a house, clothe and feed a couple of children, and get more than a couple of thousand pounds when they retire to look after themselves for the rest of their lives.

Sometimes people make a comparison between the wages and working conditions of stable staff and agricultural workers, but it's not a fair one. An agricultural worker probably gets a tied cottage, while the stable lad has to live in a hostel or in dingy digs in the village. One of the best things that Peter Walwyn has done in Lambourn is raise money for a trust to provide decent housing: it's been a great success, but it's only a start.

It's convenient and easy to blame the trainers for this situation, but it's not their fault. In an industry that is already understaffed, good lads and lasses are very hard to come by, and trainers are already paying as much as their businesses can afford to hang on to the staff they have. For trainers to pay more – and no trainer in his or her right mind does not want to pay more – they would have to charge their owners more. At present prize money is so low that owners would not stand for a significant increase, and if their costs went up they would either take their horses abroad or reduce their number of horses.

Racing is an international business, and many of the big owners will shift the focus of their operation from Britain to France or the USA if the ratio of reward to cost here continues to decrease. Small owners would simply cut back.

Get more money in at the top of the equation – prize money – and owners will be able to pay trainers more, and trainers will be able to pay their staff more. If staff levels cannot cope with Saturday night and Sunday programmes – as has been pointed out by those who oppose the restructuring of the fixture list – then no further proof is needed that the personnel shortage is about to reach crisis point.

Racing has got to get to grips with this problem before it's too late.

The sport also has to get to grips with its public image, and in this department no issue is more sensitive than the use of the whip, an area in which Jockey Club Rules have been evolving on an almost continuous basis over the last few years.

By and large people within racing are very insular and traditional about the whip, and tend to take the attitude of 'No one is going to tell us what to do' rather than the more constructive and beneficial approach of 'What can we do to make racing more attractive to a wider audience?'

The great majority of owners, trainers and jockeys, and the racing press, simply do not seem able to take on board the fact that the sight of jockeys hitting horses at the end of a race – especially a jumping race, when the horses are tired and have probably given their all – is a huge turn-off to many people who love animals and would otherwise be inclined to support racing. A minority appreciates that hitting horses does not necessarily make them run faster, and that young horses subjected to the whip during their early outings will not grow up to enjoy the racing experience.

Too many people think of races they wouldn't have won had their jockey not been able to use the whip, rather than races they would have won if the opposition hadn't had the stick. Most trainers profess to loving their horses as much as they love their children and/or dogs – but would they allow people to whip their children or dogs for no wrong-doing?

Advocates of the whip – which I would acknowledge should be carried for use in an emergency – are always going on about how jockeys need it to keep horses straight. Maybe it's true that sight of the whip can make a horse change direction, but one only has to watch a two-year-old race on the Flat to see the reality: most two-year-olds run straight until the closing stages when the jockeys start hitting them, and then they run away from the stick. That doesn't say much for the whip being necessary to keep horses straight!

So why did I throw in the towel and not carry on training somewhere else after splitting with Andrew Cohen?

The first reason is that I always felt very guilty about buying Uplands in the first place, since it was financed not by money I'd earned but by a legacy I'd received at a young age following the death of my father. It was rash to invest this in the yard, and that was not a mistake I cared to make twice.

No doubt I could have assembled forty horses, rented a yard and got by. Yet I am strongly of the opinion that if you want to do the job properly and not cut corners, the only ways that a jumping trainer can make money are by punting – which I wouldn't be very good at – or by trading in horses.

Trading as a trainer can be a rather dodgy business. You take an owner to the sales and buy him a horse. The vendor gives you 10 per cent in your back pocket. Do you declare that to your client or keep quiet? Or again: you take a client to buy a horse in which you already have a half share. Most people would think that you'd declare that interest to your owner, but plenty of trainers wouldn't. It can all be rather borderline, and over the years plenty of rumours have circulated about trainers pulling strokes on their owners – who, after all, will not know remotely as much about the ins and outs of buying horses as the trainers. In one case it was rumoured that a trainer had taken £50,000 from a horse that had been sold on to an owner.

The trainer I really admire is the one who buys a horse on spec (that is, without an owner for it), takes it home and turns it into a decent racehorse, then sells it on. There is no reason at all why such a horse should not be bought for £5,000 and sold for £105,000; but it takes balls, great skill and a fair amount of luck, as so much can go wrong.

So, in the absence of great gambling skill and of the

genius and courage to make and then sell on horses, I decided the chances were that I wouldn't make much out of it.

There are, of course, people who keep going by running a very tight ship. When I first moved to Lambourn most trainers sent out their horses in two lots, with an unlucky few lads having to ride out third lot while the others swept the yard and prepared the lunchtime feed. Only Paul Cole was forward-thinking enough to install an automatic horse-walker. Nowadays it is not uncommon for yards to have lads riding out four lots, and practically every yard has a horse-walker. Horses are not ridden out for as long as they used to be, and interval training makes them fit in less time than the old methods of good long work.

Brian Delaney, who served me so well as head lad at Uplands, always swore that the day we used automatic horse-walkers, rather than leading the horses out by hand and letting them have a pick of grass, would be the day he'd pack it in and go and run a pub. In the end we installed horse-walkers and Brian is not yet running that pub, but you can understand how he felt. Sadly, trainers have no option but to do things differently if they want to survive financially.

The second reason I quit was that I felt my commitment to the whole business was on the wane, and my failure to solve the problem of how to stop my horses getting sick had demoralised me. I was fed up with the sinking feeling in my stomach when the vet came into the office with that morning's tests. I had had enough of passing on the bad news to owners. It got so bad that there were moments when I felt that poor old Will

Pearce, the trainer who, two days after pulling off a major coup, had gone up to the gallops and shot himself, had done the right thing. Who knows what I might have done without Miriam's support?

In the end I decided that the only thing to do was to give up and make a success of something else. I could go back to training racehorses in ten years' time and still only be forty-five. There was the possibility of starting to train on the Flat, but I thought I'd sink without trace. There was only one conclusion: it was time to move on, shed a few more tears, and say goodbye. Time to shut one door and make another one open.

It's very hard to give something up rather than carry on – especially hard in the case of training racehorses, which was my whole way of life – but I had trained horses with the firm intention of getting to the very top, and had always told myself that I would stop just as soon as I realised I wasn't going to get there. I knew that I was losing that edge, that commitment which would take others to the top but not me. Any more time spent training racehorses was going to be time not getting to the top of another tree.

The problem then was exactly where that next tree would be.

It's out there somewhere.

INDEX

Note: 'CB' refers to Charlie Brooks. Horses are given in **bold** text.

WARWICKSHIRE